Appreciation for The Blossoming Heart

Robbi Zeck brings a fresh approach to the art and science of aromatherapy with her new book, The Blossoming Heart. Her aromatic artistry and engaging enthusiasm for Aromatic Kinesiology takes the reader beyond the usual application of essential oils to the metaphoric and symbolic. I would recommend The Blossoming Heart to all practitioners and students who are interested in expanding their clinical aromatic repertoire.

Dorene L. Petersen ND, Dip Acu
President, Australasian College of Health Sciences Portland USA

Robbi Zeck is an exceptionally talented and radiant being. Her work is exquisite, sensitive and inspirational. Every person can attain tremendous healing insights and awareness from The Blossoming Heart. It has been my experience that profound results can be achieved when working with her unique approach and development of aromatherapy. Your essence will definitely be enriched as your explore this beautiful gift that Robbi has to share. I encourage and invite you to venture into this magical and special realm that can be easily entered through reading The Blossoming Heart.

Ian White
author, Australian Bush Flower Essences and Bush Flower Healing

Many people have inspirational visions, many people articulate very well and many people are facilitators of great renown. What Robbi Zeck has achieved with The Blossoming Heart is to combine all three talents and the result is a work of art that you can read over and over again. This beautiful book brings the gift of rekindling your own flame of inner beauty.

Janet Ryan
Aromatherapist Perth Australia

At a time when there is such an information overload and plethora of repetitive information being published in books relating to aromatherapy, the unique style and mindful observations delivered in The Blossoming Heart are more than a breath of fresh air - they're truly aromatherapeutic 'inspirations'. Besides the other sentient insights offered throughout the book, Robbi Zeck's gentle wisdom and powerful imagery is adroitly expressed in the Essential Oil Reflections segments. This seminal work, which skilfully integrates aromatic science, metaphysics, and emotional health and healing, would be a valuable adjunct to both practitioners and students of aromatherapy and kinesiology.

Sandi Nye ND, Clinical Aromatherapist and Educator
Aromatherapeutic representative Allied Health Professions Council of South Africa

Appreciation for The Blossoming Heart

Aromatic Kinesiology is a unique combination of essential oils and energetics. It is entirely appropriate that the creator of Aromatic Kinesiology is a unique person. Robbi Zeck is a gifted teacher and therapist. At last her years of practical experience can be shared in her inspiring book, The Blossoming Heart.

John Kerr
Director, Springfields Aromatherapy and editor of Aromatherapy Today Sydney Australia

What I have observed about Robbi Zeck is that everything she puts her mind to, is carried out with great thought, beauty and the utmost grace. I have attended many of Robbi's seminars, including a delightful, women's spiritual retreat in the hills of Bali. Even here, she created the most magical and wholesome space for us to explore our inner being. The Blossoming Heart has been written with the same energy that Robbi brings to everything she touches. With heart.

Rowena Maine
Principal, Kinesiology Connection Melbourne Australia

Robbi Zeck has written a passionate and inspirational book so right for our time. To enhance the effects of traditional talk therapy, The Blossoming Heart, encourages the use of aromatic anchors through the application of essential oils. These aromatic mediums can be helpful in establishing a sense of safety and comfort while a client strives to move through emotional blocks. The Essential Oil Reflections described in The Blossoming Heart speak to the intelligence of the heart. The essence of this wisdom tells us that deep within our own stillness lies the power to regenerate and to heal. Aromas coupled with the power of imagery can unlock these healing forces and The Blossoming Heart takes us beautifully down this healing path.

Dorothy McCall, Ph D. LSW. Cert. Aroma.
Chief Executive Officer, Kingsbury Fragrances Inc. Pittsburgh USA

The Blossoming Heart is an inspiration for clinical practitioners and lay persons alike. This book helps to facilitate positive change through its gentle, yet passionate approach to using essential oils. Motivational with its refreshing aromatic style, The Blossoming Heart encourages us all to take the time for quiet reflection.

Christine Saunders
Principal, Asia-Pacific School of Aromatherapy Hong Kong

The
Blossoming
Heart

Robbi Zeck ND

Aromatherapy
for Healing and
Transformation

Copyright 2003 Robbi Zeck

First published in Australia 2004

Published by Aroma Tours

10 Keam Street East Ivanhoe Victoria 3079 Australia

Phone / Fax (03) 9499 8681

Email: info@aroma-tours.com

Web: www.aroma-tours.com

In conjunction with Brolga Publishing Pty Ltd

Email: bepublished@brolgapublishing.com.au

PO Box 12544 A'Beckett Street Melbourne 8006 Victoria Australia

Printed in Australia by Superprint

Front cover photograph: John Bragagnolo, Creative Visual Concepts

Back cover photograph: Jim Llewellyn, Aroma Tours

Graphic Design: Phil Hickey and Nikki Healy

Photography: Jim Llewellyn, John Bragagnolo and Connie McCann

Calligraphy: Jiang Yu-min

Art work: Mary Caia-Boustead

Editing: Pauline Luke and Helen Wells

National Library of Australia cataloguing – in publication data

Zeck, Robbi

The Blossoming Heart: Aromatherapy for Healing and Transformation

ISBN 0-9580959-0-6

1. Aromatherapy 2. Emotional healing 3. Essential oils 4. Health

1. Title

For Jim.
My heart to your heart.

No book is ever a sole creation and is always the product of many creative ideas. Intellectual debt must always be honoured and acknowledged as inspiration that comes from everywhere. I truly appreciate and give thanks to the many authors and teachers from whom I have learned.

For their support, belief and celebration of my process I acknowledge the following people:-

Helen Wells for her perception and spiritual clarity.

John Bragagnolo for his passion and festive heart.

Kaye Rickards for her support and loving discernment.

Jo Heriot for her wise spirit and inspirational generosity.

Phil Hickey for his creative principles and humour.

Dorothy McCall for her intuition and loving heart.

Vesna Bragagnolo for her sense of beauty and loyalty.

John Kerr for his friendship and support.

Natasha Iskandar for her sensitivity and eye for beauty.

Eric Arthur for his sincerity and wonderful depth.

Christine Saunders for her courage and commitment to excellence.

Helen Baxter for her quiet grace and warmth.

Monika Haas for her beautiful heart and spiritual generosity.

Sven Kling for his friendship and creative insights.

Caroline Kardachi for her support and unflappable administration.

Yo-June Wen for her inspiration and artistry of vision.

Marg and Doug Thornell for their loving kindness and fine wines.

Betty Caldwell for her loving friendship and compassionate heart.

Bill Bachman for his delightful wit and very fine eye.

Denise Williams for her quiet caring and superb sense of order.

John Tapper for his irreverent spirit and fine mind.

Soriel for her wisdom and the drumbeat of her soul.

Diana Padovani for her loving nature and gentle heart.

Ron Guba for his aromatic alchemy.

Karyn Jones for her spontaneity and enthusiasm.

Roger May for his dynamic and diverse view of the world.

Pia Laura for her smile that is touched by the angels.

Sally Rodd for her sparkling laughter and the rhythm of her spirit.

The Goddesses for creating the space to dance and to be still.

Jim Llewellyn for his heartfelt love, wise determination and expansive vision.

I appreciate especially my clients and seminar participants who trusted the dance as their hearts opened into an expansive way of thinking and feeling through embracing this work. Thank you.

Contents

FOREWORD

As someone who is very passionate about the therapeutic application of pure essential oils and the use of kinesiology as a practical tool of discovery and change, it is wonderful to see that my friend and colleague, Robbi Zeck, has completed her long-awaited book.

You will notice if you read one of the many books about aromatherapy today, that there is usually a list of essential oils describing all their potential uses for healing the body, mind and spirit. However, the truth is that these stated uses are seldom based on any real evidence – many of these statements are hopeful at best. And, with no large pharmaceutical companies or government bodies paying for useful research, the bulk of our knowledge will continue to come from the efforts of practitioners themselves – our own research, observation and results with clients.

Enter kinesiology, a well-established method for delving into the energetic or vibrational characteristics of remedies, in this case, pure essential oils and their capacity to help engender positive transformation in individuals.

When I first began offering practitioner training in aromatherapy and aromatic medicine in the late 1980's, Robbi was the first to offer kinesiology training as part of this course. Robbi's enthusiasm and passion for aromatherapy paved the way for the development of Aromatic Kinesiology. I happily attended her first training way back in 1990 and she has gone from strength to strength since then.

The Blossoming Heart represents a 'life distillation' of the many years of Robbi's research, consideration and experience. **The Essential Oil Reflections** are based on long observation of the results of how the living energy and character of each essential oil can serve in the process of our opening, growth and heart-focus, (instead of a head-focus). Worthy and useful research indeed.

As a tool for personal change and exploration, **The Blossoming Heart** has much to offer for your own development and also for those whose lives you touch.

I congratulate Robbi for her dedication and perseverance in putting pen and heart to paper and completing **The Blossoming Heart.** I wish this book the great success that it deserves.

Ron Guba
Director of the Centre for Aromatic Medicine
Melbourne Australia

The Blossoming Heart

We are living in times of monumental busyness. Our world is growing smaller and life is moving faster. We often feel we are spiraling out of control because life is too full of doing, doing, doing. We must achieve more, be more and acquire more. At some loosely defined point in the future we can then possibly relax and enjoy it all. Maybe! No wonder stress related illness is at an all time high. Modern living places a strain not only on our minds but on our bodies as well. *Time to be*, has become the ultimate luxury.

Amidst the turbulence, there is a quiet revolution demanding that we change the way we live our lives. We are beginning to recognise that it is imperative to stay connected to the things that harness our energies. We yearn for the tranquil moments that bring the opportunity to look inward, to reflect, reassess and replenish. We are discovering that as we reduce stress, enjoy emotional renewal and revitalise our energies, we change the way we view the world around us. We also alter our experience in our world.

What is it that makes us feel centred and balanced? How can we refresh and invigorate ourselves? How do we slow down and take the exit from the fast lane? How can we let go of busyness and experience *time to be?*

The Blossoming Heart takes us on a journey where we can take a quiet pause, embrace an environment for personal renewal and savour the simplicity and beauty of being.

The Blossoming Heart is a synthesis of my 25 years of clinical research and experience as a naturopath, kinesiologist, aromatherapist and professional trainer. **The Blossoming Heart** draws from my series of seminar programs, Aromatic Kinesiology™, and blends information, relaxation techniques, quotes and meditations to help you rekindle your own flame of inner beauty...and find your own *time to be*.

In my practice, I use the information in **The Blossoming Heart** during every consultation. It assists me in understanding my clients' viewpoint, to gain insights about why they may be experiencing stress and to offer points of reference to facilitate change. To explore any experience with depth and meaning while allowing your heart to stay open, is indeed a great gift. That gift is available for every one of us to share.

The Blossoming Heart will help you move through any of your patterns that may be holding you back from living a full and satisfying life and knowing the true essence of your heart.

Essential oils have been used since ancient times and more widely over the past two decades. They continue to grow in popularity. The most common uses for essential oils are in massage, aromatic vaporisers, the bath and natural skin care formulations.

When I began my work with Aromatic Kinesiology seminars more than fifteen years ago, essential oils were not generally used from a metaphoric or symbolic perspective. Over time, I developed a narrative style of working with essential oils that I have called **The Essential Oil Reflections.**

These reflections have been the focal point of the teachings found in Aromatic Kinesiology seminars. The story of each essential oil provides a perspective that allows an opening, a movement towards what is emerging in the soul, giving shape to the inexpressible or invisible, and sometimes touching into our own sense of the divine.

The real voyage of discovery consists not in seeking new landscapes, but in having new eyes.
Marcel Proust

In my work with Aromatic Kinesiology I see that when the human spirit is motivated through the heart, thinking and feeling become expanded, allowing an experience to be viewed in an entirely different manner. Stories are a wonderful medium that can transport metaphor and image into an evocative and transformational experience.

Stories and narratives are a part of life and always in the background of everyday conversations. The stories we tell ourselves reflect our hidden inner world and shape the decisions we make and the actions we take. Stories can provide a powerful context for creating meaning about our lives and act as a bridge from what holds us back, to moving towards what we really want.

I am writing this in the most beautiful of settings in mid-summer, at a delightful cottage on the grounds of a 19th century homestead in the Mount Macedon ranges, an hour's drive from Melbourne. Two generous friends have gifted me with a sojourn of solitude, to write in this place of quiet beauty, surrounded by their lush and enchanting garden. Majestically soaring trees, an abundance of plush purple hydrangeas and herbaceous borders of rosemary and lavender. Flowing lawns tumble their way down to a bubbling creek winding its way along the periphery of the property.

On my morning strolls I find small pockets of tantalising beauty tucked here and there. A garden statue secreted under the crook of a weeping cherry tree. A sunken pool, so beautiful that perhaps goddesses may once have lain along its chiseled edges. And now, a proud family of ducks has claimed it for their own personal bathing pool. Two ancient wrought iron chairs sit in perfect alignment side by side beneath a vine-clad pergola, surveying the order of the verdant profusion.

An eight-columned, marble rotunda, complete with heavenly doves and aptly named the Temple of the Winds, watches silently over the garden. This sturdy sentinel, surrounded by a moat filled with delicate water-lilies, has a path of tiny granite stepping stones just the right size for one sure foot, positioned over the water. I make my way across the stones and now I am standing at the centre of the Temple of the Winds.

In every direction I look there is beauty to behold and I am reminded of why I am writing this book. Wherever there is beauty, divine inspiration arrives and I feel my heart blossoming with remembered joy. I am writing because I said I would and so I must. It is important to recognise the hidden beauty in everything. There are blessings in every moment. Not only in our triumphs and apparent external beauties, but also in our sadnesses and hardships. When we meet each experience through the heart, then our essence merges with spirit and right order naturally follows.

My husband, Jim, took a quiet pause when he decided to follow his heart and end an unsatisfying business relationship that was slowly eroding his health, his joy for living and his passion for creativity. It was a tough time for him, having to turn his back on a pathology software system he had developed and its subsequent monetary rewards that were not insubstantial. He decided to follow a dream of the heart and studied saxophone for two years at college. The study totally changed his focus from systems analyst and medical technologist, to budding musician and free spirit.

During this period we were leading an Aromatic Kinesiology seminar in Bali. One idyllic day, I said in a moment of inspiration, "Let's take a group of people to the south of France to visit the fragrant lavender fields, the farmers who distill the aromatic plants and the glorious village markets. Wouldn't that be an enriching and fascinating experience?"

The very next year our group of twenty aromatic plant and perfume lovers were enthralled by the heady blend of earthiness and sensuality that is Provence. We enjoyed the most fantastic of journeys. What made this trip so astounding was that it was also our first trip to France! However, we were so clear about our vision and so committed to its positive outcome, that we went ahead and did it anyway. Later, when the timing was right, we named our specialist tour company, Aroma Tours, offering travels to awaken all of the senses.

Some might say that we were right for the time. From a gracious seed came an idea that has continued to blossom and grow, bearing luscious fruits for Aroma Tours. At various times throughout the year, we take people from all over the world on tours and retreats, to many of the delightful places on earth where aromatic plants are born.

There is a blessing in this kind of beauty. It is the beauty that comes from being aligned with your true potential. We now have a thriving business we operate together which is also connected to my clinical practice and various seminars. I am grateful everyday that we can live from our passion.

This book is about movement and change and focuses on recognising the strengths and divine purpose inherent in each of us.

Thank you and welcome to **The Blossoming Heart.**

Robbi Zeck ND

Aromatherapy and the Flowering Heart

*The perfume of sandalwood and the scents of
rose and jasmine travel only as far as the wind.
But the fragrance of goodness travels with
us through all the worlds. Like the garlands
woven from a heap of flowers, fashion
your life as a garland of beautiful deeds.*
Buddha

Aromatherapy and the Flowering Heart

The link between the sense of smell and our emotions is both deep and profound. No other sense has the ability to interface so directly with the primitive part of our mind that is the timeless seat of our moods and emotions.

Our sense of smell transports us back in time and space. On this magical journey we re-live long forgotten experiences and emotions. Today's aroma finds yesterday's aroma in our memory, bypassing the conscious mind and logic.

Smells are surer than sounds or sights to make your heart strings crack.

Rudyard Kipling

It is through these intimate connections with the primitive mind and by influencing the more subtle energies, that aromatherapy is able to have a very positive and beneficial effect on relieving stress and supporting emotional wellbeing.

A particular odour can trigger memory patterns that we may need to observe from a different perspective. The subtle quality of an essential oil can penetrate an area in our consciousness that has perhaps been fixated or limiting. This allows for a richness in understanding that we may not have experienced in the past and can lead to new possibilities.

The way we relate to a particular essential oil is a function of our physiology, experiences and value systems, so it is important to allow for variation in the way that we each may respond.

All I need do is open a bottle of rose water or lavender essential oil and I am instantly transported in my mind to stunning places of aromatic beauty. Then I become at ease and able to deal with the challenges I am facing in the moment. You may have a similar response to those aromas or a very different one from mine.

Sales and marketing people know from experience that scent sells. If two products are placed side by side on a shelf, the one that is scented will always sell more successfully. The cosmetics and perfumery industries are based on the connection between fragrance and emotions, and are always trying to create an aromatic link between their products and our emotional selves. After all, it is a feeling that they are selling rather than a product, and smell can be a very powerful ally.

The growing popularity of spas has a great deal to do with the use of natural aromatics during the treatments. The combination of a nurturing environment, tactile therapies and aromatic anchoring reinforces the spa as a place of sanctuary and deep relaxation.

The chemical properties of essential oils have been thoroughly researched yet very little is known about their energetic and emotional properties. The opportunities for using aromatherapy in a more conscious way, to help with emotional wellbeing, are yet to be significantly explored. The effect of herbal medicines and flower remedies is well documented.

As one researcher and herbalist, David Hoffman writes: *"A unique opportunity is created by the simple act of taking herbal medicines; in making a practical link with Gaia, ecological cycles for healing are activated. The door is open to the possibility of a miracle of healing way beyond the removal of disease. There can be a direct experience of ecological flow and integration, a sense of belonging in the deepest sense and of knowing that one is home, healed and whole. Such healing goes beyond the treatment of pathologies and the alleviation of bodily remedies. Rather, it is the realm of the luminous, the transformation that comes about through divine touch."*

Essential oils have brought into our lives much more than simple fragrances. All plant-based remedies have the potential to initiate an awakening of the soul. They remind us of the journey we are taking, rekindle our passion and dynamically activate the flowering of the heart. As we have become aware of the importance of aromas in our lives, a whole new concept of beauty in the environment has arrived with it.

Bathrooms everywhere are stocked with delightful soaps and spa products. Essential oil vaporisers are used widely and a sense of space, place, light, simplicity and freshness in the home and in the workplace have become a high priority. The aesthetics of fragrance surrounds us, enhancing our appreciation of all that is beautiful.

Knowing beauty can be a great healer. To draw beauty into our lives through all of the senses, can heighten and deepen our awareness of how to influence our physical health, our state of mind and our connection to spirit. The creation of beauty can transcend us into another time and place deep within our being.

Matter is the most spiritual in the perfume of plants.
Rudolf Steiner

In each little bottle of true essential oil is nature's precious gift to us for healing. Each essential oil is closely tied to the vitality and beauty of the aromatic plants themselves; those special regions where they are naturally found or cultivated and also to the dedicated people who grow and distill them with skill and passion. All that is needed is for us to unlock their hidden treasure.

What is aromatherapy?

Aromatherapy is a branch of phytotherapy or botanical medicine. Herbs, flower essences, many homeopathic remedies and traditional Chinese medicines are also phytotherapy. Aromatherapy uses essential oils from flowers, leaves, branches, barks, roots, seeds, resins and fruits. They assist the body, mind and emotions to maintain a state of balance. Essential oils are concentrated, volatile plant extracts. This means they diffuse or evaporate very quickly into the atmosphere and therefore, simply smelling an essential oil can be beneficial to your wellbeing. It is believed that essential oils and other fragrances subtly trigger the release of natural hormones in the brain, helping us to feel uplifted, or better able to cope with pain, stress and strong emotions.

The garden of the heart is moist and fresh
with jasmines, rose and cypress trees.
Rumi

Aromatherapy is not a new therapy. Plants, flowers, and their essences have been used throughout the ages in many different cultures for their medicinal and healing qualities. They were once considered precious substances and were often the basis for trade between countries. Essential oils are usually steam distilled, but may also be cold pressed as with citrus peel oils. Carbon dioxide extraction methods may also be used depending on the delicate nature of the plant.

Essential oil quality depends on many factors. The dedication of the grower, the location of where the plants are grown, how they are grown, the use of the correct species and plant part, appropriate harvesting methods and the skill required in the extraction or distillation process are all important factors. Also, the assurance that the essential oil has not been adulterated in any way prior to packaging is imperative. Some essential oils are costly to produce so the price of essential oils varies greatly.

How does aromatherapy work?

Essential oils may be chosen for their perfume or therapeutic properties. They may be calming, stimulating, antidepressant, balancing, antiviral, antibacterial, detoxifying, analgesic, tonifying, antiseptic, grounding and uplifting. Essential oils can be used in baths and foot-baths, as soothing ointments, warm compresses for skin and muscles or as inhalations for respiratory congestion. Essential oils are blended in a carrier oil when applied during a massage, to invigorate, tonify and relax the body and mind.

Aromatherapy may be used in many different ways. Electric diffusers or candle vaporisers heat and allow the essential oils to evaporate into the atmosphere. The aroma then influences your body and mind, via the sense of smell. Approximately 6-8 drops every couple of hours is usually sufficient for the average sized lounge room. Remember to place warm water in the bowl first if using a candle vaporiser. Diffusion of essential oils can be very effective when people are feeling unwell, to ease breathing, to create a pleasant atmosphere in a room, to enhance relaxation and meditation, to stimulate concentration and also to bring about a different state of mind.

As a general rule, massage blends can be created with one drop of essential oil for each 2ml of carrier oil. For a body massage, 10 drops of essential oil in 20 ml of carrier oil is appropriate. In baths 6-8 drops of essential oil is sufficient. Care must be taken to ensure that there will be no skin reaction. Some essential oils, such as citrus oils can be irritating to the skin. A capful of emulsifier already blended with your chosen essential oils can be added to the bath to reduce this possibility.

Essential oils are highly concentrated and are generally not applied directly to the skin. For this reason they are blended in a carrier oil or unscented base cream for application to the body. Essential oils are added to the carrier oil base to create a percentage dilution. The most common carrier oil is cold-pressed almond oil. Appendix three outlines how you can easily create a massage blend using the carrier oil of your choice.

Essential oils should not be taken internally unless under supervision of a doctor or a naturopath. It is also important to keep them away from the eyes. If you happen to get any in your eye then give yourself an eyebath with a little tepid water. This immediately soothes any irritation. Applying undiluted essential oils to the skin is best avoided. The exceptions are lavender and tea tree on cuts, bites and minor burns. A skin reaction to any blend can be simply treated by wiping off the essential oils with a clean, dry cloth. Then keep applying an unscented carrier oil to the area, which will soothe the skin, until it is no longer irritated.

Opinion is divided over the use of essential oils during pregnancy, although concrete evidence is still limited in this area. Some essential oils do have hormonal effects. If you really want to err on the side of caution, then do not use essential oils in massage or baths in the first three months of pregnancy without first consulting a qualified aromatherapist for their professional advice. Vaporising essential oils are of course not at issue here. See appendix four for further cautions.

Before using an essential oil always check for any contra-indications in a good reference book. There are a great many books available for general interest and also for the dedicated therapist. With due regard for their chemical concentration and a knowledge of the precautions that apply, you can explore the physical applications of aromatherapy quite safely to enhance your lifestyle. Essential oils are potent substances and need to be treated with respect.

Thinking outside of the aromatherapy box

Aromatherapy, while aiding the physical healing process, also works in the mental, emotional and spiritual areas. If you fill your time with continual doing rather than being, you may lose sight of your spiritual nature and begin to feel that something is missing from your life. The Blossoming Heart shows you how to create the space for quiet reflection about various issues you may be wanting to address at this time in your life. When you become still your soul's senses become active allowing the voice of your soul to be heard. Essential oils whisk you to another world. Here your mind is relieved of the daily stresses of life and your heart opens to a different way of seeing.

Every year I am blessed with the good fortune to lead a Women's Retreat in Bali. In this beautiful oasis, hidden away amongst the rice terraces, we undergo a gentle and loving transformation. It begins the moment we arrive and the feeling stays long after we return home. Bali is a land of offerings and blessings, filled with a rich tapestry of rituals and honours a very spiritual way of living.

One year I created an exotic aromatic perfume blended in jojoba oil, to bless each woman as she arrived at the retreat. It contained essential oils of jasmine, sandalwood, lime, lemongrass, cinnamon, clove, ylang ylang and rose. I gently anointed the forehead of each woman with this lovely perfume. This was followed by a touch at the heart with a red hibiscus flower dipped in holy water. The red hibiscus is considered a holy flower in Bali.

Ni Made Marni, a beautiful, young Balinese woman assigned to take care of us, appeared as I was giving the blessing to the women. I blessed her too with the aromatic perfume and touched her heart with the red hibiscus. She was moved to tears with the blessing as her heart fully opened to that moment. Later, she reported that she had felt a great rush of warmth move through her heart and beyond her. It did not matter that we were from different cultures. The importance was in setting the intention to open to the love and beauty that resonates in all of us. Ni Made Marni understood that clearly. And in that silent moment love was there.

When the silence falls upon us, we can hear
the voices of the Gods pointing out in the quiet
light of divine law, the true path for us to follow.
H.P.Blavatsky

When you have a strong intent about something and you believe it to the core of your being, then people will recognise the truth in what you believe. Set your intention in a congruent way. As long as your idea is connected to your heart, then you will achieve great things. Believe it and keep on believing in it. When your vision becomes integrated then others will believe it too. Doing what you love and loving what you do is integral to a blossoming heart. A heart that comes into fullness is one that is filled with light and love.

While the most common use of essential oils is through vaporising, baths and massage, there is another dimension to aromatherapy that is positively stunning. The life force of essential oils facilitates change in the physical body, however it is the spirit of the plants that touches our soul. Essential oils have the capacity to open our hearts like a blossoming flower. I have discovered that working with the principles of The Blossoming Heart gives people a way to step into a peaceful, heartfelt way of being and living. You too can do this.

May your heart's garden of awakening
bloom with a hundred flowers.
Thich Nhat Hanh

Scents of heaven, plants of earth

Throughout time, flowers, plants and herbs have been viewed as symbols of life, love, fertility and abundance. Linked with religion, their healing powers were seen as gifts from the gods and goddesses and plants were often used in ceremonial celebrations and rituals.

In ancient Egypt, the lotus or sacred water-lily, was associated with the life giving power of the Nile and with Osiris, Lord of the Dead. The Pharaohs burned incense to please the gods and were embalmed with fragrant spices, unguents and balms. The Hindus believe the god Brahma was born inside a lotus and it is revered as a sacred flower. In both Hindu and Buddhist art deities are often seated on a lotus throne.

Bali has many ceremonies, rituals and an abundance of beautiful, aromatic flowers. The significance of nature is so very powerful for the Balinese that they believe the sweeter the flower, the more quickly their prayer will go to heaven.

The Greeks were the first to develop a language of flowers known as florigraphy. Every single flower and herb used as floral decoration and adornment had an associated meaning. The Romans later adopted this system and created a festival in honor of the Goddess Flora.

Over the centuries, flowers and their meanings became associated with a wide range of human emotions, conditions, events, places and ideas. Art, literature and poetry are all richly endowed with flower symbols that speak a universal language of beauty, colour, sensuality and fragrance. Flowers have always honoured the language of love and beauty, carrying their passionate message to the soul with a stun of colour and a symphony of fragrance.

In modern times, flowers, plants and herbs have continued to be widely regarded and used in a variety of therapies as symbols of the soul to unlock our spiritual potential.

Flower essences

The 'father' of flower essence therapy, Dr Edward Bach, an English physician, recognized that those patients of a very negative or emotional nature did not progress as well with their treatments, compared to those patients who had a more balanced state of mind. To facilitate their healing, he developed a set of flower remedies based on the essences of flowers and the spirits of plants, which helped to transform negative feelings into positive ones.

Seek the outstanding mental conflict in a person.
Give them the remedy that will overcome that conflict
and all the hope and encouragement you can.
Then the virtue within them will do all the rest.
Treat the cause not the effect.
Dr. Edward Bach

Throughout the world today, flower essences and other remedies are used by therapists and lay people alike to facilitate change, healing and spiritual transformation. The healing powers of flower essences assist in raising consciousness by changing the vibratory frequency in the subtle energies.

A flower essence is an extremely diluted liquid that
contains the essence and vibrations of a flower. It is used
to bring clarity to the conscious mind and resolve negative
beliefs. Flower essences also directly effect us at the
subconscious level where we make decisions about our
emotions, health, energy, abilities, life directions and relationships.
As a result, real physical change and emotional healing occurs.
Ian White

Essential oils and The Essential Oil Reflections, also have the capacity to create a different perspective. They enable you, to emotionally and cognitively make a shift in your perception about any situation you may be experiencing. At a point of quiet reflection and detachment, you are able to clear your mind and reach greater understanding. If you are able to view every experience as a way of learning about yourself, your life will unfold with far greater possibilities. You will also draw very different experiences towards you, for your continued learning and development.

Developing awareness

There is a vast array of written information and technical data about the effects of essential oils on our health and wellbeing. Much has also been written about how we process our emotional world, deal with stress and how we can continue to find meaning and depth in lives that are constantly challenged.

You can increase your awareness of your body and mind. You can change your state of mind in an instant by accessing the senses of touch, taste, smell, sight and sound. You can experience a feeling just by looking at a picture or remembering a situation that made your heart sing. You can do a physical workout to energise your body. What is the best way you know to energise and motivate your body?

Fragrances also effect us at the subliminal level. Fragrant aromatics change and enhance our awareness as easily as looking at an image or listening to a piece of music that moves our soul.

Pause for a Blossoming Heart

- *Sit in a comfortable chair.*

- *Take a deep breath and relax your body.*

- *Remember your favourite aroma.*

- *When was the first time you smelled it?*

- *Where were you?*

- *What were you doing?*

- *Who was with you?*

My favourite aroma is grapefruit, the essential oil that initiates a movement away from feeling drained and toward greater optimism. When I smell grapefruit, its light, fruity fragrance has an uplifting effect on my mood. When I was a young girl, my neighbourhood friends had a rambling backyard planted with a glorious orchard of fruit trees. We would play in this secret garden, revelling in our own magical world and when the grapefruit tree was fruiting I was always enchanted by the tangy, fresh aroma of the sunshine yellow fruit.

Fragrant Bali Bliss

In the mid-seventies, when I first travelled to Bali my time there was a delicious sensory experience. There were the lush, green rice terraces, the tinkling sounds of gamelan music and the open hearted, smiling Balinese people. There were smells like no others I had encountered. Aromas of coconut, mango, chilli, ginger, clove, nutmeg, lemongrass, cinnamon, turmeric, tuberose, frangipani and cananga flowers, mingled with the smells of sand and sea. The heady smoke of sandalwood incense wafted in the air, along with the scents of thousands of daily offerings made to the gods. The memory of all this beauty lived at the back of my nose. Even now, I am back in Bali whenever I recall these smells. A part of me is simply at home in Bali. I relax into my deeper heart, in a peaceful environment that heightens every one of my senses. Beauty and exquisite aromas abound there.

Until I studied aromatherapy I did not know why my memory of Bali was attached so keenly to my sense of smell. Then I learned that smell and emotion are intrinsically linked. Odours impact on our emotional world, reaching into the deepest recesses of our minds and arousing strong feelings. These experiences have steered me into a rich world.

My time in Bali, my subsequent training and my professional life have led me to understand that loving what I do and doing what I love is the most powerful way to live my life. I love to share the simplicity and beauty of what I have learned.

CHAPTER TWO

The Healing Journey

It is not what you do, but how much love
you put into the doing.
Mother Teresa

The Healing Journey

Beginning with the end in mind

Writing a book is a challenging and exciting process. In order to begin, I began with the end in mind. I visualised many people reading The Blossoming Heart and having increased joy, love and beauty in their lives after applying the principles outlined. I felt it was important to bring the essence of what occurs during Aromatic Kinesiology seminars onto these pages. I drew on the principle of creating beauty so that hearts can blossom and my vision was a prayer of grace through knowing the way of the heart.

Recently, I was invited to lead a seminar in Taiwan. I was both excited and nervous about the possibility. The challenges were huge. The participants were beauty therapists and spa owners, spoke no English, knew nothing about kinesiology and were unfamiliar with working in the emotional realm. In the Chinese culture feelings and emotions are generally very private matters. My seminar manual was reduced to less than a quarter of its size and translated into Mandarin. I wondered how I would get my ideas and principles across while not losing the essence of the work in translation.

Once again, I began with the end in mind. I visualized leading the seminar like the Bali Women's Retreat, touching into the beautiful landscape of the loving heart. I set the intention for hearts to blossom and open to the soul's capacity to love. Thus began an amazing and magnificent dance of the heart with these wonderful people, and I was blessed to be working alongside a gentle and caring young woman who was my translator for my entire stay.

On the first morning, within the first hour, people were moved to tears of joy, sadness, inspiration and love. This had never happened before at the very beginning of a seminar. Even the translator was crying! We just kept moving with the beauty of the moment until the heart of the group was beating in a wondrous rhythm. Each day unfolded with blossoms of wisdom appearing seemingly from out of no-where.

I am filled with gratitude for the opportunity this experience gave me in trusting that the heart is more powerful than the mind. I clearly saw where I wanted to go and kept my attention there instead of giving in to feeling overwhelmed by the challenge. When you operate your life from your heart all boundaries are transcended, including language.

Pause for a Blossoming Heart

- *All challenges bring a blessing.*

- *No matter what the challenge there is always a gift.*

- *What blessings have come your way today?*

Curing and Healing

In my early years of being in clinical practice I read an article by a long since forgotten author, discussing the difference between curing and healing. It had a profound impact on me. It changed the way I teach, work with clients and live my life.

The author explained that healing involves education, re-assessment, changing many of the conditions under which we are living and re-examining the structure of our lives. In time I came to understand that if life is holding us back, we may need to question our habits, desires, behaviours, beliefs and even our relationships.

Healing requires that we keep on examining everything until we find our own truth and discard everything that clutters our lives. Clutter comes in many forms. The unseen clutter, lurking hidden in our psyche can be the most difficult to shift. Clutter of the mind can include worry, concern about what others think of us, negative thinking, needing to be right and focusing on things that aren't really important. Just as our sock drawer or home office will benefit from a good clearing out, our minds and our bodies also benefit from periodic sorting, sifting through what is important. This can be a positive step towards embracing stillness and *time to be*.

Curing, on the other hand, aims to restore a person to function or wholeness after the onset of illness and disease. Curing addresses toxins, invasions, degeneration, endotoxins and so on. Healing enables us to find resources that allow us to celebrate life, despite illness and disease. Healing pushes us towards a wholeness that is a process as well as a creative response. We can have a disease and not be ill. We can be ill without having a disease. Illness can also be about spiritual discomfort. Spiritual discomfort can also cause illness. When not connected to our spiritual path we are unable to utilize our spiritual resources.

In Sanskrit, the word for health is swasta, meaning to be stabilized in oneself. Health is experiencing a balanced life and a quality of stillness that comes from being centred. We heal towards the things we deeply desire, creating a movement away from any fears and concerns we might harbour. It often takes considerable courage to re-work the patterns of our lives so that we can move forward positively in life. For that to happen we need to open to greater levels of our own self-understanding. Sometimes, that desire for change and healing may be hidden or blocked deeper down in the subconscious and we need assistance to locate it.

The healing journey is a very personal process for each of us. As we move along the path, we notice changes in our inner life and in the stories we tell ourselves. We discover how to create an environment where we have integrity with ourselves and the world on a daily basis. We draw greater experience into our lives as we liberate ourselves from everything that hinders us from creating the kind of life we truly desire to live.

Pause for a Blossoming Heart

- *What clutter do you need to remove from your life and your mind?*

- *How could your health and wellbeing be improved?*

- *Do you yearn to dance to the rhythm of a different drum?*

- *What if you could choose a new direction in life?*

Life's Lingering Luxuries

In these busy times we need to stay connected to the things that bring us energy. Our time is so precious that luxurious living is taking on a different meaning. The concept of luxury now embraces time to be, spaciousness, peaceful living and the maintenance of a sustainable and intact ecology.

Integral to the healing journey is time to spend in quiet reflection and creating an environment that is healing to our bodies and our minds. The power of restoration and replenishment comes fully alive when we take a tranquil pause. From this place we can listen to the longings of the soul.

What a wonderful life I've had! I only wish I'd realized it sooner.

Colette

It is in these quiet moments that we can address the blocks that prevent us from moving forward in life. As we move towards emotional renewal and put new values in order for ourselves, we can extend that philosophy out into our community and the wider world. As we discover truly who we are and have the courage to be that, we can nurture ourselves while making a difference. Enlivened in our inner world, we can contribute to the healing that is much needed for our beautiful earth to continue to be sustained and nourished. We are all part of the one mind, the one heart, the one breath and the one consciousness.

The Blossoming Heart and Aromatic Kinesiology seminars largely speak to the part of the self that is ready to unfold. This stirring of the soul is always motivated from within and is the basis for growth, development and evolution. Lasting transformation always evolves from deeper changes within and is influenced by the age-old technologies of collective integrity and wisdom.

I have found that essential oils are great companions for the healing journey. The most primal part of the brain, the limbic system, or what is referred to as the 'emotional brain', responds to aromas in an instinctive way. Research has shown that there is a direct link between the heart and the limbic system and that the heart has its own intelligence. The heart responds to messages sent to it from the emotional brain and then calls on the brain to make appropriate responses. When the pathway between the heart and brain is clear, our resistance to change is lessened, encouraging a movement towards all that is whole. This is why I refer to the 'open heart'. My experience with essential oils has shown me over and over again, that the emotional brain and the heart are quietly influenced by fragrance.

Sourced from a bountiful array of flowers, plants, trees, seeds, spices and fruits, essential oils offer their own insights, transformations and healings. It has been my privilege to facilitate people as their hearts have been gently opened through this work. As surely as a blossom unfurls when the time is right to share its beauty, there is also a right timing for the sharing of information and quiet reflections.

Then, as we make our way along the stepping stones of life, essential oils assist us to gently integrate any changes taking place.

Pause for a Blossoming Heart

• *When was the last time you felt inspired to make a change?*

• *Is there a tiny change you could make in your life?*

• *How would this change allow you to bloom?*

• *What is one thing that you would like to heal towards?*

• *Which essential oil could support this change?*

CHAPTER THREE

Essential Oils and Emotional Metaphor

*Self-care is never a selfish act. It is simply good
stewardship of the only gift I have.
The gift I was put on earth to offer to others.
Anytime we can listen to true self, and give
it the care it requires, we do so not
only for ourselves, but also for
the many others whose lives we touch.*
Parker Palmer

Essential Oils and Emotional Metaphor

Enhancing your lifestyle with essential oils is a superb way to take care of your own health and wellbeing. Each essential oil has a story to tell and the Essential Oil Reflections can be referred to when you are seeking a different perspective on life matters. During consultations with clients, I have found that the symbolic expressions of essential oils enhance their capacity to look at life differently. Clients more easily release symptoms, restore balance and open into a broader way of thinking and feeling. The Essential Oil Reflections offer a pathway to gaining a deeper understanding of our journey through life. In Eastern traditions, the wisdom of the mind is located in the heart. When we listen to the heart we discover ways of tapping into our far-reaching sources of wisdom.

Symbols of all kinds, both modern and ancient, can provide the remedies needed for healing. Carl Jung regarded the process of reclaiming the soul as the experience of becoming at one with God. He believed that this was the only way for us to ultimately heal all inner conflicts and eventually discover, that in fact, we are ONE.

Symbols are healing the gap between higher consciousness and us. Enter into the magic of psyche and experience deep transformation.

Carl Jung

The subtle quality of an essential oil can penetrate an area of our consciousness that has been stuck, allowing us to view a situation from a different perspective. The purpose of each Essential Oil Reflection is to enhance our awareness of an aspect of life that we may need to change or embrace differently. Each of the Essential Oil Reflections awakens the recognition of the pertinence of all our encounters and assists in reframing emotional issues. The challenge around understanding the concept of the Essential Oil Reflections is its unfamiliarity. Understanding the concept will enable you to create more useful strategies during times of stress or misunderstanding.

The Essential Oil Reflections have the ability to relieve emotional stress and release any negative patterns that may be contributing to physical symptoms. The intention is to bring equilibrium to the physical body, restore emotional wellbeing and encourage your heart to blossom.

Essential Oils and Aromatic Anchoring

We are all familiar with how the sense of smell can whisk us back into the past and that a long forgotten memory can emerge when we smell a particular odour. When I was young I would walk up the driveway of our home to meet the baker's van. As the smiling baker threw open his doors, the glorious smell of the freshly baked golden loaves wafted out. My mother would buy a family loaf and I would choose a crusty bread roll bursting with flavour for my lunch. So deliciously satisfying! I loved that smell and I still do. This is aromatic anchoring in action. It is a reminder for the central nervous system to respond in a particular way.

Research shows that there is a strong relationship between olfaction, memory, mood, emotion and thought. Essential oils have the potential to affect positive change through the olfactory/mind link but each person has a unique set of experiences that flavours their responses to a given situation.

Dr Candace Pert, the author of **Molecules of Emotion**, discovered with her groundbreaking research that there are chemicals of emotion. In fact, every emotion is attached to a chemical and our body has to vibrate at a certain frequency to experience an emotion. Emotion is associated with how the tissues vibrate. To change the way we feel about something, we have to change the vibratory rate of our body. Emotion could be described simply as energy in motion.

Aromas, emotions and memory are closely interwoven. Aromatic anchoring can be valuable in changing present time perceptions, creating new options and allowing positive behavioural changes. Essential oils have the capacity to touch at the core of the soul effecting the deeper, unconscious mind, dissolving old emotional patterns. The energetic qualities of essential oils play an important role in stimulating the body's electromagnetic fields, to activate the natural healing process. The higher consciousness is always drawn to colour, sound and fragrance for their vibrational healing qualities.

Like any art, the creation of self is both natural and seemingly impossible. It requires training as well as magic.

Holly Neur

A fragrance can influence you enormously on all levels from the etheric to the physical and educate your system to function at a higher, more aware level. A fragrance can place you into a finer frequency as you set new goals to align your higher process.

The meaning we give to something shapes our attitude towards it. For that reason you will not find the same essential oil being required when people are going through similar experiences. Physical illness and stress are often emotionally based. Each person has their own individual and unique way of experiencing their inner world. Therefore, their emotional responses will vary. In my experience, physical illness always has an associated component of unresolved emotional stress.

There are many practical ways to relieve stress, support our emotional wellbeing and keep our energies vibrant and clear. Everything begins with a spark of an idea. Words, images and also fragrances have the potential to change our awareness profoundly. Many essential oils have the capacity to reduce emotional stress. However, the essential oils profiled in The Blossoming Heart may differ from those that are more typically used to relieve stress. When I am consulting with a client, I choose the most appropriate Essential Oil Reflection relative to the issues we are exploring. From a symbolic point of view the reflection looks at a person's life journey from an emotional, spiritual and heart-centred perspective.

The Essential Oil Reflections can:

• *Convey a message about where you currently stand in life.*

• *Create a deeper understanding about your life experiences.*

• *Draw on the emotional qualities of the essential oils.*

• *Invite the possibility of emotional renewal.*

• *Assist in releasing negative patterns associated with physical symptoms*

• *Explore new options and expand your thinking.*

• *Increase your ability to listen to all parts of the self with compassion.*

• *Bring serenity to your soul.*

• *Open your heart to the fullness of love.*

• *Offer space and time for quiet reflection.*

How to Utilize the Essential Oil Reflections.

The metaphor is probably the most fertile power possessed by man.
Ortega Y. Gasset

As you read the Essential Oil Reflection, a different quality of awareness will emerge about the underlying issues that may be at play in a particular situation in your life. These life issues may or may not consciously stress you. To gain the most insight when reading the information, relate it back to what is going on in your life. For example, ask yourself how you are feeling. Do you have a physical illness? Is your life going according to plan right now? Are you concerned about your family or professional life?

There are various ways to utilise the essential oil information. If you are familiar with kinesiology or energy testing of the body you can use that method to choose the Essential Oil Reflection and essential oil.

You can scan through the Aromatic Emotional Barometer chart to clarify how you are feeling or thinking and then look up the appropriate Essential Oil Reflection.

You can simply choose an essential oil that you feel drawn to for the day; then read the Essential Oil Reflection and let this random piece of information stimulate your thinking and your feeling, so that you begin to look at your situation in a different way.

Or, after identifying a situation in your life that you would like greater clarification about, intuitively you can choose an Essential Oil Reflection by opening the book at random and then reading the description you find there.

Each Essential Oil Reflection has an associated pair of key words. These key words bring to your awareness very quickly, the emotional quality or state of mind that you need to change. Because we know that the heart and brain are linked, words, as well as aromas, trigger the brain to effect the intelligence of the heart. The essential oils have both a positive and a negative emotional attribute and offer the potential to shift you from a negative frame of mind to a positive state of being.

The Essential Oil Reflection also weaves a story about the emotional qualities of the essential oil. A series of questions is found at the end of each reflection. To regularly ask yourself insightful, meaningful and critical questions enables you to expand your point of view. There is an art to quiet reflection. When pondering the questions, simply wait and notice your thoughts and feelings as you allow an answer to arise. This directs you to arrive at a new place of understanding and awareness. Questioning directionalizes your thinking, sets an intention for change and can reshape the quality of your life.

Once you have chosen the essential oil, place a drop on a tissue so that you can smell it throughout the day. Enhance the ambience of your environment using a vaporiser. Smelling the essential oil as you go about your day will begin to anchor some new behaviours and thoughts.

You may also like to use the essential oil by placing a few drops in the bath, in a massage blend, or take the chosen oil with you to your next massage or aromatherapy appointment.

Wonder is the promise of restoration:
as deeply as you dive, so may you rise.
Christina Baldwin

Roses in Provence

Our time together after the tours finish in Provence is always special to us. Jim and I meander around the countryside exploring and never tire of gazing at the beauty of the purple lavender undulating in the fields.

Driving along a picturesque, winding road, Jim and I followed a series of tiny, hand-made signs to an exquisite old abbey set high upon a windswept hilltop overlooking a gorge. Here, in the most unlikely of places, was a floral park bursting with fragrance and blossoms. More than five hundred varieties of magnificent roses, a superb array of bonsai trees, a colourful display of annuals and gnarled old olive trees were all cheerfully presided over by a collection of large crystals placed about the garden. We were astounded. Then we met Serge, who was a walking testament to someone living his dream. Speaking in French and sign language, we learned that he had searched for five years before he found this property. For years he had looked for his dream and then one day, his dream found him. In the raw stillness of the old ruins he felt his heart blossom with joy and knew he was home.

Joined by three other couples, Serge, and his wife began an amazing transformation of the old abbey, the little chapel and the land that has since grown into a floral park. They all have an affinity with roses, which symbolise a sense of belonging, an awakening of the heart energy and spiritual renaissance.

The 12th century chapel has been painstakingly and lovingly restored to its former grandeur. The vault in the chapel has been completed, right down to the finest gilding on the architraves. The altar is made of a hand-hewn slab of marble. Placed upon the altar, and flanked by candelabras, is the most beautiful rose quartz crystal I have ever seen. In days gone by, altars were commonly placed against the back wall of the vault and the priest would face away from the congregation. Serge and his friends felt strongly that the altar should be placed directly under the center of the dome. A visiting historical architect sternly informed them that this was most incorrect.

Several months after the altar had been positioned in the centre, it was the day of the winter solstice. At the opposite end of the vaulted dome, high above the chapel door, is a small round window. At that stage it had no stained glass in place. The sun came shining through the opening, pouring its golden light directly onto the altar, lighting up the rose quartz crystal. Jean-Yves who had been working in the chapel that day ran to get the others and they marvelled at the incredible sight. Nowadays, on both winter and summer solstice, musical recitals are held in the chapel, as the acoustics are superb.

Over the years we have become firm friends with these dedicated folk. In the summer of the year 2000 we took our first group on a specially arranged visit and since then the abbey is always a favourite with our groups.

Serge had a dream that came to him as a tiny seed, it went on to blossom and then developed into fruit. His vision was to be a caretaker and healer of a parcel of land that could be nurtured back into the fullness of life. The land of course has gone on to sustain others and is a beautiful biodynamic oasis for the glorious rose garden.

To be affected by the things that make a difference in our lives, to be profoundly moved by beauty, to care about something greater than our concerns, reminds us that the heart is indeed more powerful than the mind.

All the flowers of all the tomorrows are in the seeds of today.
Indian Proverb

Pause for a Blossoming Heart

To blossom means to bloom, open, unfold, flower, evolve, mature, flourish. Think for a moment about how your life is unfolding at this time. The light and shade of life is equally important and each moment, even a crisis, can open you to many gifts and possibilities. How will you know when your heart is blossoming? This simple exercise will help you sustain your own blossoming heart.

- *What is your definition of a blossoming heart?*

- *How do you feel when your heart is blossoming?*

- *What gifts do you have that are seeded from your heart?*

- *What are the circumstances in your life that trigger your blossoming heart?*

- *How do you sustain your blossoming heart?*

- *What rituals could you embrace to enhance your blossoming heart?*

- *Which essential oil enables you to feel connected to your blossoming heart?*

- *What do you do that supports the hearts of others to bloom?*

- *If you were to draw your blossoming heart what would it look like?*

CHAPTER FOUR

The Aromatic Emotional Barometer

Your vision will become clear only when you look into your own heart. Who looks inside, dreams, who looks inside, awakens.
Carl Jung

The Aromatic Emotional Barometer

I was being challenged with an aspect of writing The Blossoming Heart. Although surrounded by positive, encouraging, supportive people, I felt quite emotionally flat, uninspired and uncreative.

One frustrating evening, I looked at the Aromatic Emotional Barometer chart and the paired words, Rational/Confused and Creative/Stuck, jumped out at me. The two related essential oils are Lemon and Rosemary. I certainly desired to be rational and creative. I no longer wanted to feel confused and stuck. I blended these essential oils in a carrier oil and applied it to my wrists, my feet and the back of my head, just at the base of my skull. I tucked myself into bed, read the Lemon and the Rosemary Essential Oil Reflection and invited my night mind to dissipate the stress I was experiencing.

Before I went to sleep I imagined what it might be like if I were The Blossoming Heart. How would it feel to have someone reading me? How could I be more visually appealing? How could I stand out from all the other books? In what way did I want my message to come across? What could I say that would allow hearts to softly blossom? How could I be seen as a refreshing tonic to my readers?

The next morning the difference was truly remarkable. I awoke feeling refreshed and renewed with the creative juices flowing like a thundering waterfall. I placed a few drops of Lemon and Rosemary in a vaporiser to subtly enhance my writing environment. I wrote all day long, as if I had the wind at my back propelling me effortlessly along. I felt grateful to be resourceful once again and able to get on track with my vision for that final, elusive chapter.

It takes a different quality of consciousness to solve a problem than the kind of consciousness that created it. By changing the geography of our mind and inner life, we place ourselves in a higher frequency. Fragrances can help old emotional patterns to fall away and reduce the emotional charge around current stressful issues. It is easy to create a powerful change like this and you can do it too. When your energies are clear and vibrant, what you make a shift towards shifts towards you.

How do we gauge how we are tracking in our life? Our internal compass is set to keep us on track. When we become stressed our tracking mechanism can go awry. Just as a compass always shows the direction of true north, our internal compass is one that instinctively tells us that we are headed in the right direction. The Aromatic Emotional Barometer is an easy way of mapping what we need to do to create a movement away from feeling stressed.

On the following pages you will find the Aromatic Emotional Barometer chart. The essential oils and the pairs of key words are grouped under the spiritual, emotional, mental and physical bodies. The chart is usually produced as a single page, in colour and laminated for ease of use. However, in this book, each group is listed separately to make the chart easier to read. If you are drawn to using an essential oil you may prefer to just think about the paired key words rather than read the entire Essential Oil Reflection. Using the specific essential oil associated with the paired words, helps to free up your energies and gets you moving along again.

However, if you do not have the essential oil at hand, it is still useful and valid to reflect on the information about it. The essential oil can always be obtained later from your local supplier.

The Aromatic Emotional Barometer chart was developed over a period of time, mapping clients' emotions and moods, alongside certain words and essential oils that correlated with their experiences and feelings. We have all the resources we need in order to make changes. It is just a matter of accessing those resources to assist us in shifting towards a different state of mind and heart. Once our awareness is heightened then we can choose to move from a present state of mind, to a more positive state of being. Our life blossoms when we can shift gear from thinking negatively to expecting the best.

Spiritual

Supported	CYPRESS	Challenged
Tranquil	ELEMI	Restless
Protected	FRANKINCENSE	Vulnerable
Trusting	JASMINE	Fearful
Nurtured	LAVENDER	Neglected
Grateful	MELISSA	Resentful
Illuminated	MYRTLE	Disheartened
Choice	NEROLI	No choice
Peaceful	PATCHOULI	Fragmented
Loved	ROSE	Isolated
Receptive	ROSEWOOD	Hindered
Wise	SAGE	Unknowing
Reflective	SANDALWOOD	Entrenched

Emotional

Yielding	**BENZOIN**	Resistant
Encouraged	**BERGAMOT**	Saddened
Connected	**CINNAMON**	Withdrawn
Attuned	**GERANIUM**	Disconnected
Joyful	**JUNIPER**	Distressed
Calm	**LIME**	Agitated
Soothed	**MARJORAM**	Anxious
Lighthearted	**ORANGE**	Serious
Compassion	**PALMAROSA**	Betrayed
Worthy	**PINE**	Inadequate
Motivated	**SPRUCE**	Defeated
Assurance	**VETIVER**	Threatened
Mindful	**YLANG YLANG**	Angry

Mental

Perceptive	ANISEED MYRTLE	Incapable
Expressive	BASIL	Insecure
Courage	CEDARWOOD	Cautious
Freedom	G.CHAMOMILE	Imposed upon
Clarity	CLARY SAGE	Stagnant
Open	CLOVE BUD	Controlling
Integrated	EUCALYPTUS	Overwhelmed
Complete	FENNEL	Unfulfilled
Optimistic	GRAPEFRUIT	Drained
Rational	LEMON	Confused
Expanded	LEMONGRASS	Restricted
Awakened	PETITGRAIN	Stifled
Creative	ROSEMARY	Stuck

Physical

Assertive	ANGELICA	Unacceptable
Restored	CISTUS	Shocked
Adaptable	EVERLASTING	Immobilised
Sustained	GINGER	Depleted
Safe	KUNZEA	Hurt
Revitalised	NUTMEG	Conquered
Purposeful	PEPPERMINT	Unfocused
Definite	RAVENSARA	Tentative
Invigorated	SPEARMINT	Weary
Dynamic	THYME	Powerless
Understanding	TEA TREE	Intolerant
Productive	WINTERGREEN	Inert
Balanced	YARROW	Erratic

CHAPTER FIVE

Blossoming Heart Affirmations

The most beautiful and most profound emotion we can experience is the sensation of the mystical. It is the power of all true science.
Albert Einstein

Blossoming Heart Affirmations

A Blossoming Heart Affirmation has been created for each Essential Oil Reflection. Affirmations are short positive statements that describe a specific outcome. Create your own. Write them down and repeat them to yourself regularly. Some people like to place their affirmations on the fridge or above their computers so that they look at them often. Even though you may be engrossed in another activity, such as cooking a meal or writing a letter, your consciousness is still working for you when you take an affirming approach to life. Find a place that you look at daily to display your affirmations.

Think about your life's big plan. What do you really want to do, have and be in your life? Create a personal vision to keep yourself motivated and energised about your plan. When writing down your goals and affirmations, be as specific as you can be. State them in the present tense as if you have already achieved the desired result. Make your vision come to life so that you can feel it with all of your senses. Review them regularly, even daily and they will align you with your passion for living.

If you, for example, are concerned with issues of trust read the Essential Oil Reflection for Jasmine. The Blossoming Heart Affirmation is *I trust myself, bless the present and expect the best*. Repeating this statement for a period of time, writing it down and smelling the Jasmine will effectively impress your subconscious mind. It will direct your thinking to produce the result described in the affirmation. When mental images are related to all the senses, particularly to the sense of smell, an affirmation becomes far more powerful.

At the end of each Essential Oil Reflection you will find the Blossoming Heart Affirmation. You may even enjoy creating your own affirmation if there is an element of the wording that appeals to you more. The affirmation combined with using an essential oil as an aromatic anchor will produce outstanding results.

In my own life, Blossoming Heart Affirmations help me to focus and to stay on track. For example, my affirmation for writing this book has been *I create beauty and hearts blossom* and I have been saying this to myself for a year or two now. In this case, my vision has taken that long to come to fruition. Remember, the results are not always instantaneous so don't give up after the first few days, even if nothing seems to be happening. Myrtle, the essential oil I chose to support my affirmation, is about illumination and beauty. It expresses a movement away from separation and a movement towards the recognition that we are all born connected. Myrtle brings the gift of seeing oneself in a new light.

Since beginning to write The Blossoming Heart, what I have noticed about people attending the seminars is a beauty that rises in each person. The quality is so tangible that at times it takes my breath away.

There are also times when the results of saying affirmations, combined with using essential oils can seem miraculous. Jan came for a consultation several weeks after tearing her hamstring badly while out walking. Her physiotherapist said the damage was as severe as a football injury. As I talked with her it became apparent that there were some life issues that needed to be addressed. Jan was feeling lonely and withdrawn and had recently retired. Energy testing of the body indicated that Cinnamon would bring some relief to her painful leg. Cinnamon offers a sense of connection and a movement away from withdrawal and separation. *I am connected to the present moment* is the Blossoming Heart Affirmation for Cinnamon. I blended 7 drops of Cinnamon essential oil in 15 ml of almond oil, which Jan applied to her hamstring several times during that day. She also repeated the affirmation often. When she woke the next morning she was pain free. Coincidence or miracle? Jan was not concerned about that, she was simply glad to be moving without pain.

Pause for a Blossoming Heart

I find it useful to have a few extra strategies at hand to keep my heart open and my plans flowing along with grace and clarity. Here are some ideas for you to incorporate into your daily routine.

- *Create beauty in the environment in which you live.*

- *Say something positive or smile to at least one person every day.*

- *Do what you love and love what you do.*

- *Clear out your clutter.*

- *Undertake regular bodywork and inner-work to keep your nervous system clear.*

- *Recognise your gifts and talents.*

- *Every evening before sleeping, acknowledge all that you are grateful for.*

- *Make the time to be quiet and to be still.*

- *Every morning on waking, say thank you for another day of living and loving.*

- *Play, have fun, laugh.*

- *Open to love and the sensation of beauty within you.*

- *Regularly review your goals and make one step toward them every day.*

- *Celebrate your wins, big or small.*

- *Show the people you love, your love.*

CHAPTER SIX

The Essential
Oil Reflections

You ask why I make my home in the mountain forest,
and I smile, and am silent,
even my soul remains quiet,
it lives in another world which no-one owns.
The peach trees blossom,
The water flows.
Li Po

Angelica - Root Angelica archangelica

Assertive - Unacceptable

It is not because things are difficult that we do not dare;
it is because we do not dare that they are difficult.

Seneca

  herb, root and rhizomes

  earthy, spicy, balsamic

  1

Standing tall in nature, Angelica bursts with power and energy, growing up to two metres tall. It has a thick main stem and a strong root system, deeply embedded in the earth.

Angelica brings a fiery action to the physical vitality and can assist in strengthening your resolve and to follow through with your convictions. Angelica encourages you to stand your ground, to assert and to express your truth and confidence.

Learn to express yourself assertively using the following simple, yet effective formula. It will help you to send a clear message to another person, identifying your thoughts, your feelings, your wants and what you are willing to do about a particular situation. Practise writing the formula down first and then put it into action. It will be a useful tool to explore areas of your life, where you feel unacceptable to others and when you are feeling held back in some way.

I think...I feel...I want...I am willing...

When you find yourself at a crossroad, unable to go back or move forward and this position in life is unacceptable to you, use Angelica to access the strength and endurance to forge the way ahead.

- *Do you have any behaviours that are unacceptable even to yourself?*
- *Where do you need to be more assertive in your life?*

♥ Blossoming Heart Affirmation

I assert myself with confidence and ease.

Aniseed Myrtle Backhousia anisata

Perceptive - Incapable

Why not go out on a limb. That's where the fruit is.
Will Rogers

tree, leaves and stems

anise and liquorice-like

2

Aniseed Myrtle assimilates life experiences and brings things into fruition. The seeds for your direction in life lie within and must come from the inside out. Re-awaken your imaginative quest. Bring your vision into manifestation to enable you to move forward in life.

Build up your risk muscle and begin to think outside the box when new ideas need to be developed. Change your mental channels and keep your risk muscle in shape by trying something different. When you are out of sync with your life plans and you feel incapable of pushing through, Aniseed Myrtle will access another layer of perception to carry you along.

Aniseed Myrtle is useful for gastric disturbances that can occur when your pace is too fast and you feel harried and stressed. Slow down, take a mental health day, tune in and take a wider look at your life situation. Choose to be in the now so that your perceptive awareness is heightened.

Aniseed Myrtle brings stamina to new ideas born in non-conforming environments.

• *What new thing would you like to try in your life but haven't yet?*

• *What are you willing to do to put your ideas into action?*

• *What aspect in your life is requiring assimilation?*

♥ Blossoming Heart Affirmation

What I make a shift towards, shifts towards me.

Basil Ocimum basilicum

Expressive - Insecure

Listen closely to the voice that speaks to you each day,
open up your heart and mind and hear what it has to say.

Inner Voices, Sweet Honey in the Rock

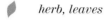 *herb, leaves*

 fresh, peppery, spicy

1

The sharp spicy fragrance of Basil brings balance and clarity to the inner emotions as the need to control falls away. Let your heart speak, take a risk and express yourself.

Basil helps the throat and heart centres to open with ease allowing a movement away from fear and insecurity.

Listen for the true note of your self-expression and journey to your creative heart. Find security in expressing yourself through the creative arts, learn to speak out and trust the guidance of your intuition. Bring your true and authentic essence forward.

Let your inner voice be your guide and allow Basil to set the tone of your internal dialogue. Basil is a wonderful reminder about the power of positive thinking and will generate a greater sense of security as you affirm and express yourself positively.

* *Where do you find security?*
* *What do you need to give voice to in your life?*

♥ Blossoming Heart Affirmation

I am secure and self-expressive.

Benzoin Styrax benzoin

Yielding - Resistant

"I always get my own way." "Hmm! How do you do that?"
"I change my way."
Larry Quick

🔥 *tree, resin*

💧 *sweet, vanilla-like, rich, intense*

💧 *4*

As surely as the dawn emerges and the earth celebrates the warmth of the sun, the vanilla-like fragrance of Benzoin determinedly brushes away resistance to change. Benzoin seeps deeply into any dark interior alcoves that may feel unyielding, solid and stuck.

When there is a challenge in accepting new situations and you need to abandon a familiar position, notice where your resistance lies. Benzoin helps you to acknowledge and integrate what has been changing in your life.

To change the direction in which you are travelling requires a process of adjustment and commitment. Benzoin brings you into alignment with change. When we change, all things change. Learn to celebrate the changes.

* *What changes in your life do you fear or resist the most?*
* *How can you yield to what life brings you?*

♥ Blossoming Heart Affirmation

Change becomes me.

Bergamot Citrus bergamia

Encouraged - Saddened

*May there be light for you in dark places
when all other lights go out.*
J.R.R. Tolkein

🍃 *tree, fruit peel*

💧 *sweet, citrus, fresh, green, light*

💧 *10*

Bergamot brings a sunny, effervescent quality to the spirit through balancing the hypothalamus gland, the centre-spring of some of the deeper emotions, particularly qualities of fear and rage.

Our lives are patterned with ever changing vistas of light and shade. The passages of darkness and the shadow energies in our lives can also be our greatest teachers. Remember that there are blessings in discomfort if you choose to examine why your spirit is flat, sad or depressed. During these times of dark reflection Bergamot will heal and cheer your soul, encouraging you to continue to explore your deeper innermost feelings.

Inhale the cheery fragrance of Bergamot and make a space deep inside yourself where there is room for light. This interior place is where the golden glow of your spirit resides. Encourage the irresistible lightness of being to be braided through your soul. Experience yourself as the scent of light.

* *What are the best ways you know to lift yourself away from depression and sadness?*
* *How do you encourage yourself to move forward?*

♥ Blossoming Heart Affirmation

As my heart opens love and light enter.

Cedarwood Cedrus atlantica

Courage - Cautious

You must do the thing you think you cannot do.
Eleanor Roosevelt

tree, wood and chips

warm, woody, balsamic

5

Subtly embedded in the woody fragrance of Cedarwood is the resonance of courage. The grounding quality of Cedarwood brings recognition of safe passage enabling you to fully embrace the next phase of your life.

If you are erring on the side of caution and ignoring an important call to a new, different and inspirational way of living, then dare to stretch your wings and move forward in life with courage.

It often requires considerable courage to rework the patterns of our lives and Cedarwood brings strength and commitment to that desire. Deeply consider and contemplate your soul's journey where healing and higher learning has occurred.

• *Are there some courageous conversations you need to have that will re-create your personal destiny?*

• *Where does your courage rest within you?*

• *What gives you the courage to take action?*

♥ Blossoming Heart Affirmation

I embrace my courageous heart.

69

Chamomile - German Matricaria recutita

Freedom - Imposed upon

We must be willing to get rid of the life we've planned
so as to have the life that is waiting for us.
Joseph Campbell

 herb, flowers

 bitter-sweet, floral, herby

 2

German Chamomile helps to loosen the grip of old habits, ideas and beliefs that are no longer useful in living the life you want to live. Imagine your life speaking to you. Consider what it would say.

Let go of things that girdle your life and move beyond any self-imposed limitations. You may be aware of tightness or tension in your body. Notice where you are holding on or holding in. Take a breath. Let go.

Personal freedom begins with the privilege of thinking differently. Explore the freedom in choosing new adventures, create a different consciousness and soar to new heights. Let the scent of freedom hover at the wings of your soul.

German Chamomile promotes a letting go of the old and stale so that the fresh and new can evolve. German Chamomile heightens your ability to simply let go, relax and go with the flow when circumstances surprise you and plans change. Let go and let be.

• *Are you living the kind of life that your life truly wants to live?*

• *If your life were to speak to you what would it say?*

• *What do you need to let go of or release from your life*
  to bring you fully alive?

• *Where do you find freedom?*

♥ Blossoming Heart Affirmation

I let go and let be.

Cinnamon - Bark Cinnamomum zeylanicum

Connected - Withdrawn

*The light of God flows into receptive angel hands and the angel is
ever ready to pour the light into our hearts if we hold them open.*

Lothar Schreyer

🌢 *tree, bark*

🌢 *strong, spicy*

🌢 *5*

When you are feeling emotionally withdrawn and living in
a state of separation, Cinnamon trickles into the vast, deep, inner
world, bringing warmth, energy and a sense of connection to the
present moment.

The ultimate spiritual journey is to dare to explore your inner
resources and then act on your own interior guidance. Listen to
what your deepest self has to say and find a thread of connection
that will lead you away from any feelings of separation.

If you are struggling to stay connected know that all relationships
have phases of contraction and expansion. You may need to cultivate
a different way of expressing yourself and connecting with others.
Learn to transform your struggles and upsets into sweet moments.
Stay connected to the light and stay in the present moment.

- *What part of your body harbours withdrawal and
  separation?*
- *What activities make you feel the most connected?*
- *What is it that you long to be connected to?*

♥ Blossoming Heart Affirmation

I am connected to the present moment.

Cistus Cistus ladaniferus

Restored - Shocked

If you want the honest spiritual truth my prayer is this:
Dear God, get me out of this mess.
Rita Mae Brown

 shrub, leaves and stems

 intense, musky, fiery, sweet

1

The fragrance of Cistus is warmly settling and quietens the physical, mental, emotional and spiritual bodies. Useful after any traumatic event to hold the heart steady, Cistus brings warmth and comfort in times of emotional stress, shock and accidents.

Although crisis can be catastrophic, it can also occur in slow motion over a period of time. Crisis enables you to rise up to deal with an issue. It can also be seen as an initiation into new beginnings and new understandings. Cistus softens the effects of emotional pain and eases the pressure of a heavy heart. Gently rub Cistus over your heart centre to bring serenity to your soul in the midst of crisis.

Cistus will restore what has been hurt, healing deep down in your consciousness and flowing outward to any parts of you that may feel shattered. Make the time to talk things through with someone or do some journal writing to explore the painful shadows, opening the way for you to take a step towards a new dawn.

Know that your life challenges build spiritual muscle and that difficulties can be met and overcome. Everything has two sides and for every drawback there is a benefit. All life experiences serve us one way or another and we call these experiences to us for a higher learning that may not be immediately apparent.

• *What truly restores you?*

• *Ask yourself, how does this experience serve me?*

♥ Blossoming Heart Affirmation

Every experience is a great teacher.

Clary Sage Salvia sclarea

Clarity - Stagnant

To work magic is to weave the unseen forces into form; to soar beyond sight; to explore the uncharted dream realm of the hidden reality.

Starhawk

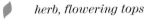 *herb, flowering tops*

 sweet, floral, nutty, mellow

4

Clary Sage switches on the inner lights, caresses the creative mind, awakens your sensory perception and broadens your intuitive horizons.

When feeling stagnant and unable to have clear understanding, Clary Sage with its liquid light, shifts you to your dream time world where your fingers can touch the tapestry of your dreams. Here, you can open to the clear insights of your heart and deeper mind. Dreams are the very language of the unconscious and can provide a resolution to any inner conflicts or a lack of movement forward in life. Ask for clarity in your dreams. See yourself flowing with the vibrancy of an active, buoyant inner life. Clary Sage heightens your natural intuitive clarity.

Clary Sage enables you to access deeper parts of the subconscious as you explore options and sift through information, leading to inspired decision-making.

- *What decision are you currently facing?*
- *How will your life take shape once the decision has been made?*
- *What insights do your dreams bring?*

♥ Blossoming Heart Affirmation

My intuition is bright and clear.

Clove Bud Eugenia caryophyllata

Open - Controlling

The only difference between an extra-ordinary life and an ordinary life is the extra-ordinary pleasures you find in ordinary things.

Veronique Vienne

tree, flower buds (dried)

spicy, peppery, sweet, fragrant

2

Need a different perspective on life? Is your life congested and filled with all manner of clutter. Don't know where to start clearing out? Then take hold of Clove Bud and surrender your control.

Clove Bud helps to loosen your attachment to material things and to your ideas about how life is or should be lived. Clove Bud heightens inner strengths when external and internal environments need to change.

Too much clutter can inhibit you from being open to new possibilities. Remove any obstacles to the flow of harmonious energy in your life and become a designated clutter free zone. Open up, become liberated from any false attachments and be more effective in your life.

When you hang on to things for longer than you need them congestion will occur. Accumulated effects you physically, mentally, emotionally and spiritually. Clear out your clutter and create the space for different opportunities and experiences to enter your life. Find pleasure in the simple things in life.

* *In which areas of your life do you feel the most congestion?*
* *What are you attached to that needs to be released?*
* *Where does control create a problem for you in life?*
* *How can you open yourself fully to what life brings you?*

♥ Blossoming Heart Affirmation

I am a designated clutter free zone.

Cypress Cupressus sempervirens

Supported - Challenged

And the day came when the risk to remain tight in the bud
was more painful than the risk it took to blossom.

Anais Nin

tree, needles, twigs

woody, balsamic, pine-like

5

When change is imminent, Cypress brings structure, strength and a sense of protection.

When you are consciously ready to move forward in life, sometimes that momentum and desire may be challenged.

Major life transitions will often involve a bottoming out emotionally and spiritually, bringing a sense of disenchantment and disillusionment. The past and the future seem to be dynamically opposed in the present moment. What is known is falling away, and what will be, has not yet emerged. During these times, you will be required to navigate a way out of that state and in order to navigate properly you need to identify your resources for change. Perhaps explore the development of visions, symbols, dreams and totems as a way of supporting yourself, when times are tough.

As challenges are met during this evolutionary movement forward, Cypress supports and holds the space for the soul to remain in balance. Support will come from everywhere, you simply need to find your voice and ask!

- *What challenge are you currently facing?*
- *What kind of support do you require to negotiate your way through the challenges?*
- *How can you create a support system around you?*

♥ Blossoming Heart Affirmation

Life supports me.

Elemi Canarium luzonicum

Tranquil - Restless

Nothing in all creation is so like God as stillness.
Meister Eckhart

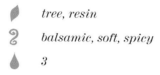

tree, resin

balsamic, soft, spicy

3

Like a quiet ripple on a secluded pond, the spicy woodiness of Elemi activates the meditative state. Elemi propels you inward to look deeply into things in order to see their nature, adding a tranquil touch.

Your inner world draws into it a fragrant stillness when the soul is shining. Elemi reflects this serenity. When your spirit is restless there can be a great emptiness, a mindless rushing about and living a life devoid of true meaning.

Settle yourself down and enter into the sacred well of stillness where the rhythmic influence of your quieter self resides and make the time for quiet reflection.

Take the time daily to still your mind, quietly brush your spirit, relinquish control and use your breath to connect to the rhythm of your own heartsong.

- *What could you eliminate from your life that would shift you from restlessness to tranquillity?*
- *What do you need to spend time meditating on?*
- *Where do you find quiet?*

♥ Blossoming Heart Affirmation

I invoke love through stillness.

Eucalyptus Eucalyptus radiata

Integrated - Overwhelmed

*You can't depend on your judgement
when your imagination is out of flow.*
Mark Twain

tree, leaves

fresh, camphor-like, cooling

3

When your thinking processes become bogged down with details, the refreshing, stimulating influence of Eucalyptus sorts individual bits of information and establishes an awareness of how all those many details will fit into the overall picture.

Develop a strategic system for handling the details of life in order to achieve consistent results. When all the facets are converted to an organised structure then your performance will be greatly improved. Learn to ask for clarification of instructions and make planning a priority. Master strategic foresight! Get organised, create systems and plan ahead.

Use Eucalyptus when you are overwhelmed with the many components in your life that require attention. Eucalyptus will encourage your mind to discover an appropriate way to respond to situations, rather than over-reacting when your ability to respond is diminished. The answer that arises from an integrated state of mind will always be the most beneficial.

Breathe in the stimulating aroma of Eucalyptus and imagine oxygen being received by every cell in your body expanding and integrating your thinking processes.

- *What aspect in your life is requiring integration?*
- *How could greater organisation move you away from overwhelm?*
- *What planning do you need to do?*

♥ Blossoming Heart Affirmation

I plan, I clarify, I integrate.

Everlasting Helichrysum italicum

Adaptable - Immobilised

If you just set people in motion they'll heal themselves.

Gabrielle Roth

 herb, flowering tops

 green, herby, spicy, warm

 1

When you are knotted-up inside and unable to stop thinking, the earthy, warming aroma of Everlasting unravels the tension that develops from thoughts going round and round.

If you are one of the walking wounded, yet immobilised by your thinking and your feelings, then use Everlasting to ground you. Stay in touch with your surroundings and remain connected to the earth. Move your body and exercise daily. The more physical skills and activities you engage in, the more flexibility and strength you will have for performing with greater stamina.

Everlasting will assist you to adjust your attitudes and behaviours. It will steer you towards steadiness, adaptability and contentment. Be prepared to abandon your plan! The more flexible your behaviour the greater control you will have over your environment, both internally and externally.

If you have hurt yourself, Everlasting will also soothe any bruising and reduce inflammation.

* *Where do you feel immobilised in your life?*
* *In what areas would you benefit from being more adaptable and flexible?*

♥ Blossoming Heart Affirmation

Adaptation creates movement and flow.

Fennel Foeniculum vulgare

Complete - Unfulfilled

*Just as we learn how to start and not finish,
we can learn to complete what we begin.*

Sark

🌿 *herb, seeds*

❷ *anise-like, sweet, peppery*

💧 *2*

The sweetness of Fennel assists in completing things that are unfinished or requiring further attention in your life. If you are feeling unfulfilled, take a look at what may be holding you back from moving forward.

Unfinished business requires closure to set the next part of your cycle in motion. When various aspects of your life move into completion, the time is then ripe for creating and meeting your highest possibilities.

When things are fully completed you reach the end of a cycle knowing that there is nothing more to be done. As a way closes, a way opens and the new can begin with a fresh vibrancy.

Fennel brings a quiet dedication and concentration to the attainment of your goals, particularly in relationship to work and tasks. Commit your energies to living in the spirit of excellence, stay focused and produce results. Fennel keeps your mind concentrated on a particular direction and accesses the quiet containment of continuity.

- *What is your mind concentrating on currently?*
- *How can you bring closure to things in your life that are unfinished?*
- *What is there still for you to heal, love, say and do?*

♥ Blossoming Heart Affirmation

I complete what I begin.

79

Frankincense Boswellia carterii

Protected - Vulnerable

*The perfection, the potentiality of the loveliness that is in everything,
is inevitable. The eternal star brings all processes to their appointed
end, and presides over our voyage through life.*

N.Sri Ram

 tree, resin

 balsamic, sweet, fresh, light

💧 *4*

A deeply penetrating, spicy, fragrance, Frankincense cleanses the aura, is finely attuned to the subtle energies and paves the way to the higher self. Frankincense deepens and slows the rhythm of the breath, providing safe passage to the inner realms of the unconscious during meditation.

Frankincense brings stability and insulation when the inner landscape of the heart is feeling vulnerable. When you feel yourself wide open, choose to stay connected to the light and know that the unseen helpers will protect you.

Our lives are patterned as one continuous voyage moving through many horizons. Frankincense will sustain you on your journey and cultivate positive inner guidance so that your true self can be seen. Honour your requirement for protection and create a ceremony or ritual to invoke the presence of your inner protector.

• *In what area of your life do you take risks or not?*

• *When are you at your most vulnerable?*

• *When do you feel the most protected?*

♥ Blossoming Heart Affirmation

I am protected by the fragrance of love and light.

Geranium Pelargonium graveolens

Attuned - Disconnected

*There is a time for everything and
a season for every activity under heaven.*

Ecclesiastes 3:2

 *shrub, leaves*

 floral, fresh, green, sweet

3

Geranium has a refreshing scent that gently reduces extremes within the inner thought processes bringing balance and harmony to the emotions. The body's natural rhythm is linked to hormonal activity and Geranium helps to tone the vibration of the glands and hormones, allowing your body to undulate in gentle equilibrium.

When you are disconnected from your rhythm, up one minute down the next, feeling out of sorts, out of sync with your internal compass and unable to map your own progress, Geranium will serenely attune you to a new tempo.

The movement of the sun, the moon, the tides and the seasons shapes our lives and Geranium connects us to these fundamental rhythms. Just like the seasons our lives move in phases of growth, falling away, disappearing and re-emerging. In your own time, rhythm, pace and grace, you will move through an infinite number of these phases. If you are feeling disconnected from the rhythm of your life, explore which season you are moving through now.

Perhaps you are in a springtime phase of your life. Here new life is present in potential and you are ready to burst forth, blossoming into fullness. Perhaps you are in a winter phase where life feels dormant and dull. Even nature has a rest every winter. And while the earth is resting, the flowers always know that they will bloom again.

- *Do you take notice and value the dormant or quiet times in your life?*
- *What are the things you naturally do to develop greater attunement to your own rhythms?*

♥ Blossoming Heart Affirmation

I am attuned to the rhythm of my life.

Ginger Zingiber officinale

Sustained - Depleted

Never give in. Never give in. Never give in.
Winston Churchill

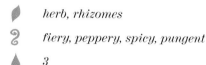

herb, rhizomes

fiery, peppery, spicy, pungent

3

The warming nature of Ginger sustains and then rebuilds where there has been a loss of energy on the physical and emotional levels.

Ginger is particularly useful when the physical body has become depleted over a period of time, giving way to feelings of melancholy and grief for oneself. When you are not lasting the distance Ginger builds the strength and endurance to succeed.

Ginger is a great tonic for restoring and balancing your energies. It opens you to being sustained in every moment. If your circulation is sluggish and you suffer from the cold, Ginger creates warmth activating the metabolism and raising the body temperature.

Rebuild your energy by taking gentle walks in nature, drink ginger tea made with slices of fresh ginger and hot water. Add a few drops of ginger oil to a warm footbath to encourage healthy circulation of the chi.

* *How has your energy been diminished and depleted?*
* *What do you need to do differently to preserve and conserve your energy?*
* *What is it that sustains you at the core level of your being?*

♥ Blossoming Heart Affirmation

I am sustained in every moment.

Grapefruit Citrus paradisi

Optimistic - Drained

No snowflake ever falls in the wrong place.
Zen saying

🌢 *tree, fruit rind*

💧 *sweet, warm, citrus*

🌢 *4*

When you are feeling drained, strung out and depressed, Grapefruit provides a new zest for life. With its light, fruity aroma it gives wings to feelings of heaviness, uplifts sagging spirits and radiates optimism. Learn from your obstacles and cultivate the ability to remain open to the moment.

Grapefruit directs your thinking toward the positive aspects of your life and the golden opportunities that are waiting in the wings. Follow your bliss and allow the hidden treasures of your spirit to be revealed.

Know that what you truly need in life has already been given to you. Your greatest strengths come from your capacity to think, understand and feel as you experience life's breadth and depth. The ability to appreciate all that you have will generate greater optimism.

Life is essentially refreshingly sweet and Grapefruit brings the gift of appreciation. Live your life consciously every moment and take full advantage of every single day.

- *What aspects of your life are draining you?*
- *Where do you feel drained in your body?*
- *What is it that you appreciate most about your life?*

♥ Blossoming Heart Affirmation

I appreciate all that I have.

Jasmine Jasminum officinale

Trusting - Fearful

With deep faith we light up the incense of our heart.
Thich Nhat Hanh

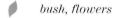 *bush, flowers*

floral, exotic, sensual, sweet

2

Like the waters of a meandering river, Jasmine penetrates the deepest layers of your soul, allaying your fears, embracing spirit and culminating in divine inspiration; a simple knowing of all that is.

When you are faced with seemingly unresolvable emotional challenges and feeling fearful, the exotic beauty of Jasmine will dissolve those fears, tenderly building trust while pouring its jewelled light into your heart.

Sit with your fears and concerns, take a breath and another and another. Wait in the stillness. An answer will arise. Prayer and deep faith will open you to trusting yourself, blessing the present and expecting the best.

Open your heart to the temple of the winds and let trust enfold itself softly around you. Imagine being swathed in a blanket of velvet that has been woven with the fragrant threads of a deep and abiding faith.

* *Is there an action that you need to take that would move you beyond your fear or concerns?*
* *Is there a hidden benefit to your fear?*
* *What can you trust about yourself?*

♥ Blossoming Heart Affirmation

I trust myself, expect the best and bless the present.

Juniper Juniperus communis

Joyful - Distressed

The soul should always stand ajar,
ready to welcome the ecstatic experience.
Emily Dickinson

bush, berries

balsamic, woody, fresh, peppery

4

When your environment requires a clearer vibration, the sharp powerful scent of Juniper will purify the atmosphere, dispelling unwanted or negative thoughts from your mind and cleanse your body.

When you are feeling distressed and shut off from the experience of joy in your body and in your life, Juniper prepares the way for finding your centre. Juniper brings clarification and stability during times of emotional and spiritual challenge. It is particularly useful when tears and fears are abundant and self-confidence is at a low ebb. Juniper reduces the negativity stemming from habits, beliefs and behaviours that rob you of your joy of life.

Juniper enhances the capacity for you to generate your own joy cultivating a more joyful internal atmosphere deep within your being. Savour the simple splendours of life and connect to a place within yourself where joy comes hurtling through your soul.

Breathe in joy and take a quiet moment to imagine joy flowing to all parts of your being.

• *Where does joy reside in your own body?*
• *Have you had enough joy?*

♥ Blossoming Heart Affirmation

Joy cascades through me.

Kunzea Kunzea ambigua

Safe - Hurt

We must embrace pain and use it as fuel for our journey.
Kenji Miyazawa

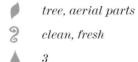

tree, aerial parts

clean, fresh

3

When you need to transform pain and inflammation, Kunzea reaches inward and soothes acute as well as persistent knots of suffering. When your body feels strung out and tight as a drum Kunzea relieves muscular aches, joint pain and nervous tension.

Kunzea also helps to defuse deep emotional pain that has grown solid as a result of suppression, creating internal blocks in the body's meridian system. Pain and crisis are part of the human cycle and mindful awareness can transform pain. Pain in the body indicates that something is wrong. Pain can also activate growth and a potential for healing. Pain is often the opening through which you can learn to trust yourself and see yourself differently. Learn to breathe your spirit fully into life. Use your breath to move you through the fear of pain and the pain of fear.

There is no such thing as an event or a pain without a feeling associated with it. Where there is pain in the body, there is always an emotion attached to the pain. Kunzea assists in the release of physical and emotional pain and in transforming the immediate shock of accidents.

- *What important conversations do you need to have in order to move beyond your life hurts?*
- *Ask yourself what will heal your pain?*

♥ Blossoming Heart Affirmation

I breathe in...I breathe out...I am safe.

Lavender Lavandula angustifolia

Nurtured - Neglected

You have a solemn obligation to take care of yourself because you never know when the world will need you.

Rabbi Hillel

shrub, flowering tops

sweet, floral, herby, soft

7

Lavender warms the heart and steadies the emotions through promoting awareness of the need to nurture oneself while travelling on the river of life.

Lavender honours the higher spiritual realms and weaves its fragrant, mauve magic through a spiral dance between the chakras.

Gentle lavender provides a cushion for life's rainy days, encouraging a level of deep questioning about what you truly need to take genuine care of yourself. Perhaps you are always looking after the needs and requirements of everyone else, to the exclusion of your own emotional care and wellbeing. Imagine what it would be like to give yourself your own undivided, dedicated attention.

Where there has been self-neglect and lack of self-care wearing away the health and energy of your body, Lavender brings nourishment and heartening reassurance.

* *Do you regularly take time out for quality self-nurturing?*
* *What truly nourishes you?*
* *How do you nurture yourself?*

♥ Blossoming Heart Affirmation

I caringly nourish and nurture myself.

87

Lemon Citrus limonum

Rational - Confused

We cannot adjust the wind but we can adjust the sails.

Anonymous

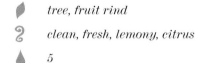

tree, fruit rind

clean, fresh, lemony, citrus

5

Fresh, tingling Lemon with its sharp and scintillating aroma, activates the hippocampus and stimulates left brain thinking.

If you are feeling confused and out of your depth, Lemon's bracing and enlivening affect upon the senses will sharpen your progress, clear your head and pave the way for rational thinking.

Confusion can bring irrational emotional outbursts and such behaviours are usually not welcomed or tolerated by others. Lemon helps to cut through confusion and is a delightfully aromatic spa for the brain.

You may need to develop new and innovative behaviours that will enhance the way you learn, execute tasks and deal with stress. Take a step back and examine what you are dealing with. The vibrant warmth of Lemon enhances rational, logical thinking and any intellectual pursuits.

Throughout the day drink plenty of water with slices of lemon to keep you fully hydrated, alert and switched on. Lemon is uplifting to your brain, enlivens your body and keeps your energies humming along.

* *Is there something you are confused about?*
* *Does that confusion inhibit you from achieving an outcome?*
* *If you are behaving irrationally, how does it serve or hinder you?*

♥ Blossoming Heart Affirmation

My thinking is clear and concise.

Lemongrass Cymbopogon citratus

Expanded - Restricted

What we need is more people who specialize in the impossible.
Theodore Roethke

grass, aerial plant parts

strongly lemony, slightly herby

2

The intense, radiant energy of Lemongrass inspires expansion on all levels. Whenever there is a sense of restriction or limitation in life, Lemongrass lifts the spirits and gets things moving again.

Lemongrass enables the mind to shift towards fascination about what is possible, encouraging you to embark on a glorious voyage of discovery. Imagine the circumference of your life experience expanding. If something has been achieved out in the wider world then know that it is possible for you to achieve it too.

Change the patterns of your restrictions. Visualise having unlimited access to all that you require to expand your stance in life. Lemongrass motivates you to move beyond any limitations and opens the way for you to step into your best possible future. Live your dreams!

- *In what ways do you limit yourself?*
- *When you think about your future what do you see,
  hear or feel wafting around inside you?*
- *What would you truly love to do with your life?*

♥ Blossoming Heart Affirmation

If it's possible in the world, it's possible for me.

Lime Citrus medica

Calm - Agitated

How we spend our days is, of course, how we spend our lives.

Annie Dillard

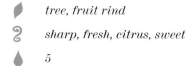

    tree, fruit rind

    sharp, fresh, citrus, sweet

    5

When you are feeling agitated, in great turmoil or dealing with stressful situations, Lime clears any heated emotions and returns you to a place of calm and ease.

The tangy, bright fragrance of Lime settles, calms and refreshes the emotions, allowing feelings to be explored and released constructively.

Let your soul be cradled within the fragrant symphony of Lime. Cultivate a sanctuary of harmony and simplicity in your environment. A sensory space to enliven your heart and soul. A healing place to rest your mind, where you can breathe freely and feel relaxed in tranquil surroundings.

- *Do you need to learn how to respond calmly when you are stressed?*
- *Which environments make you feel whole and connected in your daily life?*
- *How can you bring more calm into your life?*

♥ Blossoming Heart Affirmation

I make the time for quiet reflection.

Marjoram Origanum majorana

Soothed - Anxious

Hope is the thing with feathers that perches in the soul.

Emily Dickinson

herb, flowering aerial parts

warm, nutty, slightly peppery

3

When too much work, stress and emotional upheaval sweeps you along the torrent of life the mind and nervous system can become overwrought. Marjoram's warm herbal aroma will strengthen your nervous system, rebuild your reserve, fortify your spirit and reduce obsessive thinking.

Imagine having a nest of comforts and the items that you might place in there. Creature comforts help to minimise stress when emotional turbulence and challenging circumstances arise. Marjoram draws you slowly inward to a place of soothing comfort, healing and relaxation. Listen to your body, make some changes in your life and take the time to rest.

* *Where does your anxiety stem from?*
* *Is there a gift that comes with the anxiety?*
* *In this busy modern life what are your favourite ways to soothe yourself?*
* *How do you like to comfort others?*

♥ Blossoming Heart Affirmation

I rest and restore.

91

Melissa Melissa officinalis

Grateful - Resentful

If you have only one breath left use it to say thank you.

Pam Brown

 herb, leaves

 fresh, lemony, green, herby

 6

Like a beam of light on a dark winter's day, Melissa softens extreme emotions, eases resentment, gladdens the heart and engages the soul in its own graceful rhythm.

Reaching inward, caressing the inner being, the warm radiance of Melissa directs the spirit toward mindful reflection on all that you have to be grateful for. Breathe in the fresh, light scent of Melissa and let gratitude open you to the treasures of your heart.

The song of your own heart's knowledge will be revealed to the universe as you give thanks and offer blessings for another day of loving and living. Consider a daily ritual of gratefulness. Light a candle, burn some incense and create an offering with a fragrant flower to set the tone for your day. Say thank you often!

Melissa connects you to your place of grace. Give yourself the gift of listening to your heart and know that paradise resides here.

* *Are there any resentments lurking in the vast corridors of your mind that inhibit your gladness for living?*
* *If your heart could speak right now what would it whisper back to you?*
* *What is it that fills your heart with grace?*

♥ Blossoming Heart Affirmation

Paradise is an attitude of the heart.

92

Myrtle - Green Myrtus communis

Illuminated - Disheartened

Give me beauty in the inward soul,
and may the outer be at one.
Socrates

🌢 *shrub, flowering tips of branches*

2 *fresh, herby, camphor-like balsamic*

🌢 *4*

During dark times, when you are in pain, struggling or feeling disheartened, gentle Myrtle with its air of beauty and purity brings comfort and an elemental return to the source.

To illuminate means to light up or to shine out and Myrtle brings the gift of seeing oneself in a new light. Like a shining beacon Myrtle touches the soul with a refreshing innocence, radiating the beauty of life.

When you are experiencing feelings of separation, use Myrtle as a reminder that we are all born connected. We are indeed, all of the one mind, the one heart, the one breath and the one consciousness.

In the monastery of the fragrant flower Myrtle breathes its beautiful, soft fragrance into sacred space. Allow your daily life to become your temple by creating a sanctuary of beauty and peace.

Walk in your own beauty and be at one with all things. May there always be beauty around you, above you, below you and within you. Know that you are the gift who shines beauty and light out to others.

- *What brings beauty into your life?*
- *How is beauty expressed?*
- *Who showed you how to see and create beauty in the world?*
- *How can you cultivate the beautiful?*

♥ Blossoming Heart Affirmation

I create beauty and hearts blossom.

Neroli Citrus aurantium var. amara - flowers

Choice - No choice

*The life we want is not merely the one we have chosen
and made. It is the one we must be choosing and making.*

Wendell Berry

🝔 *tree, flowers*

𝟤 *delicate, floral, soft, sweet*

🝔 *3*

Trusting the emotional intelligence that guides the choices you make is an essential component of your natural expression. The delightfully sweet scent of Neroli fosters these choices building bridges between the inner realms where renewed life force takes place.

Reshape your life patterns as you access the calm knowing of your higher, deeper self and begin to live in the new and broader story of your life.

Neroli's fragrance is deeply embedded in the psyche and offers a quality of emotional renewal through making different and empowered choices. A choice point is any place in your life where you would like to behave differently. Know that making choices from a quiet, spacious place within will always provide the best option in the moment.

Consider the choices you have made. All choice creates consequence. Even not choosing is still a choice you make. Your choices today shape the passage of your tomorrows.

- *What significant choices in your life have influenced
  your personal evolution?*
- *Do you need to make some choices that would stretch you?*

♥ Blossoming Heart Affirmation

I make my choices from the stillpoint within.

Nutmeg Myristica fagrans

Revitalized - Conquered

All disease is the result of inhibited soul life. The art of the healer consists in releasing the soul so that its life can flow through the form.

Alice Bailey

tree, fruit kernel

sweet, spicy, slightly musky

7

When there has been a draining away or loss of physical energy from the body, due to illness, accidents or long standing stress, tangy, spicy Nutmeg, strengthens, stimulates and revitalizes the body.

When there is heaviness, sluggishness, a feeling of being conquered and unable to face the tasks ahead, Nutmeg stokes the fire, intensifies the energy and provides hearty warmth with its glowing heat. Nutmeg rekindles the flame of your life force leaving you spiritually cleansed and physically rejuvenated.

Increase your physical pursuits to increase your fitness levels and devise a routine that relaxes your muscles. Drink water, add a drop of revitalising Nutmeg to the bath, have a regular massage, stretch your body, meditate and eat energising foods.

- *What are the ways you have been inhibiting the flow of your life?*
- *How can you heal from any exhaustion you may feel?*
- *What brings vitality into your life?*

♥ Blossoming Heart Affirmation

I am revitalised by my inner flame.

Orange - Sweet Citrus sinensis

Light-hearted - Serious

Perhaps it was the flowers that made me a painter.

Monet

 tree, fruit rind

 sweet, tangy, citrus, fresh

4

Orange will help you to loosen up and find your sense of humour when you are feeling gloomy and unable to see the light at the end of the tunnel. Sometimes you may not even have an explanation for why you feel that way.

When you are taking life too seriously and there is a need to lighten up, use Orange to access a bubbling light-heartedness and radiant, inner warmth.

If you are overloaded with worry it is impossible to stay in the present moment. Your life energy will leak from you if your thoughts constantly spiral towards your past and your future. Use your breath and a mantra to keep you in the present moment.

Breathing in, I am in the present moment.

Breathing out, my heart opens.

Begin the practice of lifting up the corners of the mouth and hold for three breaths. Repeat this practice several times throughout the day and send your brain a new and happy message. It will make a surprising difference to your body and your mind.

Let humour stretch your thinking. Be languid, lighten your spirits, laugh heartily, tell jokes, read humourous stories, watch funny movies or visit a comedy club.

Like a perfumed cascade of flowers in spring, Orange brings moments of laughter and touchstones of happiness to a beaming heart.

• *How can you manifest more lightness into your life?*

• *What makes your heart merry?*

♥ Blossoming Heart Affirmation

I focus on the flowers and fruits of life.

Palmarosa Cymbopogon martinii

Compassion - Betrayed

It is compassion, then, that is the best protection; it is also, as the great masters of the past have always known, the source of all healing.

Sogyal Rinpoche

grass, whole plant

floral, sweet, grassy, rosy

8

When you have been wounded by betrayals and feel set adrift from your moorings, the gentle green scent of Palmarosa takes you on an inward journey, allowing your wounded soul to be healed and cherished.

Palmarosa opens the doorway of the heart to bring love and forgiveness to traumatic events. As you explore the meaning of any betrayal with wisdom and deeper understanding, you will move towards compassionate awareness of yourself and others.

Forgiveness means redefining loyalties, strengthening vulnerabilities and leaving behind your pain. There may be those whom you need to forgive, including yourself, to enable you to move on kindly and compassionately. You may also need to acknowledge that you need more time to process how you feel. Forgiveness will come in its own right time.

Bring strength to your vulnerability by loosening your connection to the past. Quietly clear out your inner world and choose to be more in the present moment. Take time out for spiritual replenishment, slow down, go on retreat, pray, take charge of yourself, embark on a cleansing diet and exercise regime, meditate, determine your priorities and maintain yourself in a new way.

* *Is there a betrayal or a wounding in your life that could be viewed as a pathway, leading you into a life that unfolds in a completely different way?*
* *What gift does the betrayal bring?*
* *How do you show compassion to yourself or others?*

♥ Blossoming Heart Affirmation

Compassion is the food that feeds my soul.

Patchouli Pogostemon cablin

Peaceful - Fragmented

May the moon and stars pour their healing lights on you.
Deep peace of a quiet earth to you.

Celtic Blessing

- *plant, leaves*
- *rich, earthy, musty, woody*
- *5*

The rich, musty, woody scent of Patchouli awakens within the soul a deep yearning for the comforting presence of peace, bringing spiritual insights to all realms.

Patchouli's slow peacefulness brings about a state of mind and wholehearted feeling where unification occurs with the soul on all levels.

When the fragments of your spirit have been scattered far and wide, call the peacemaker of your soul to you. Enter into the corridors of your interior world, soar beyond any self-imposed barriers and trust the rhythm of the dance.

Place your hands over your heart, allow each quiet breath you take to be peaceful and invite the deep peace of a quiet earth into your being.

A mantra of peace can become a source of great spiritual nourishment. There are many different mantras. Recite a mantra daily and let peace be the way as you follow the familiar rhythm of your breath.

Breathing in, I embrace peace.

Breathing out, I know I am peaceful.

- *What nourishes peace in your inner world?*
- *Where do you feel fragmented in your body?*
- *How can you invite peace into your world on a daily basis?*

♥ Blossoming Heart Affirmation

Peace flows through me.

Peppermint Mentha piperita

Purposeful - Unfocused

*Let yourself be silently drawn
by the pull of what you really love.*

Rumi

herb, leaves

cool, fresh, clean, minty

1

The patterns of your purpose are embedded deeply within you and truly recognising your purpose can be a transformational and evocative journey.

Peppermint assists in reconnecting you to your vital passion, whisking you away upon the winds of purpose. It focuses your desire to extend yourself as a driving force and brings your mind to a place of excellence and symmetry, propelling you forward and upward.

Icy, cool, stimulating Peppermint sustains the energy required to maintain an inner attention on your highest potential, bringing balance and focus to your own idea of purpose.

Achievement of goals comes through specific focus management, not time management. Being unfocused can turn you away from your bigger dream.

When you are living passionately on purpose, the direction of your life will change. Peppermint assists in the digestion of the idea of living a life that is purposefully on track. It is time to love what you do and do what you love. Feel the pull of your purpose resonating through your being as a passionate heartbeat.

- *In what areas of your life do you need greater focus?*
- *What is your purpose?*
- *How do you envision your future?*
- *What choices can you make daily to support your deepest passions?*

♥ Blossoming Heart Affirmation

I am loving what I do and doing what I love.

Petitgrain Bigarade Citrus aurantium

Awakened - Stifled

Deep is the longing for the land of your memories
and the dwelling place of your deeper desires.
Kahil Gibran

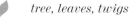 *tree, leaves, twigs*

 citrus, light, piquant, fresh

💧 *5*

The fresh, stimulating aroma of Petitgrain drifts across the pathways of the conscious mind, encouraging your memory to lead you in deeper awakening.

Your memories create the blueprint of your individual expression. Petitgrain opens the memory gaining entrance to the place within consciousness where far memories reside. Surrender to the awareness that is beyond conscious thought. Let this frontier bring new insights to illuminate your path through life.

Shine the light of awareness upon yourself and open your mind to where the soul unfurls like a blossoming flower. Here lies the deeper dream.

* *What are your ancient memories?*
* *What elements within you are ready to awaken?*

♥ Blossoming Heart Affirmation

I shine in the essence of my awareness.

Pine Pinus sylvestris

Worthy - Inadequate

*Our sense of worth is the single most important determinant
of the health, abundance and joy we allow into our lives.*

Dan Millman

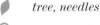

tree, needles

resinous, fresh

4

Enduring and rooted firmly in the ground, branches stretching skyward, Pine with its warm, rich, resinous fragrance, brings strength to the manifestation energy.

As the sap flows to give life to the radiant Pine, so does it kindle the flame of quiet understanding of your unique expression of life. Perhaps your heritage has been hidden and waiting to bloom under the care of a flourishing self-esteem.

Pine validates and strengthens your own unique gifts and talents encouraging a simple knowing and belief of your self-worth. Know that you are worthy of having all your dreams come true. See your own goodness and care for yourself as if you were someone whom you dearly love and cherish.

It is important to live in a way that brings out the best in you. Discover the bliss of your own being and cultivate the flower within. Understand that you are enough, know that you do matter and believe in your own significance.

• *How do you celebrate what you love about yourself?*

• *What are you most proud of?*

• *Is there an area in your life where you feel inadequate?*

• *What is your greatest accomplishment?*

♥ Blossoming Heart Affirmation

I believe in my own significance.

Ravensara Ravensara aromatica

Definite - Tentative

*Before I built a wall I'd ask to know
what I was walling in or walling out.*
Robert Frost

 tree, leaves

fresh, sharp, clear,

4

Ravensara, with its Eucalyptus-like aroma, encourages the setting of personal boundaries. A boundary delineates what is included within as well as what is excluded.

Learning to define your boundaries determines your identity and maintaining healthy boundaries is absolutely integral to your self-empowerment. Your emotional and physical wellbeing will be compromised if your boundaries are unstructured. Learn to say no! And remember, 'no' is a complete sentence.

Make a stand for yourself. Identify where you need to be more empowered. Move away from being too tentative, set some boundaries and be committed to maintaining them. By becoming aware of your own needs and educating others about how to treat you well, a true caring of your self and others can develop.

Try this exercise if you need some help in establishing boundaries. Imagine drawing a circle. Place yourself inside it. Place the people who challenge your boundaries at a designated spot outside of the circle. Some may be a placed in the outer limits and others closer to the edge of the circle. Practise visualizing this. Then, whenever you meet those people again in real life, your boundaries will be much clearer and you will feel more empowered and confident.

You can practise this idea, substituting people for any unwellness you are experiencing and also, your own irritating behaviours and irksome habits that drain and deplete your energies.

- *Is there an area in your life where you feel taken advantage of in your relationships?*
- *Do you find it difficult to say "no"?*
- *How could you set different boundaries?*

♥ Blossoming Heart Affirmation

My boundaries are clearly defined.

Rose Rosa damascena

Loved - Isolated

The lover visible, and the Beloved invisible,
whoever saw such a love in all the world.

Rumi

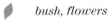 *bush, flowers*

floral, rich, heady, soft

2

Since ancient times, the mystical Rose has been used as a symbol of the soul, evoking the essence of spiritual renaissance. This queen amongst flowers contains the most precious of all heavenly scents. The glorious Rose enfolds the soul within its own fragrant song, aligning it with the higher angelic realms.

It is the nature of human love to provide the pattern through which whole-heartedness and divine love can flow. Awakening the heart energy, the exquisite fragrance of the velvety rose calls forth a sense of deeper identity and belonging.

During the times when you feel unloved and isolated, contemplate if you are not being loving enough in your world. Often unhappy moments are really a mirror for us to learn a new way of being and invite a call to action to attract greater love into our lives. Undertake loving practice. It is important to show the people you love, your love.

Our most meaningful journeys need to be undertaken alone, in a solitary fashion. And yet, from that point of quiet isolation comes an alchemy that can transform our spiritual life. The word **alone** was once treated as two words meaning all one. Aloneness can bring a great gift as we take refuge in the sanctuary of silence. Take a sacred pause, reflect deeply, authentically and quietly caress your softly blossoming heart. The rose of life and love spirals in fragrant celebration as you fully embrace the divine Beloved within.

- *How often do you take a sacred pause to look quietly and deeply at the fabric of your life?*
- *What is it that you love so much that it takes your breath away?*

♥ Blossoming Heart Affirmation

I surrender into the fragrant nectar of my heart.

Rosemary
Rosmarinus officinalis - ct cineole

Creative - Stuck

The important thing is to create.
Nothing else matters; creation is everything.

Pablo Picasso

 herb, flowering tops, leaves

sharp, fresh, herby, slightly woody

3

Rosemary, with its pungent and penetrating fragrance, assists the dynamic of development and transformation through directing creative energy into action.

When familiar patterns, conditions, habits and beliefs keep resurfacing and manifesting in your life, Rosemary moves you onward, freeing you from restriction, sluggishness and mental fatigue.

Like a tiny seedpod of creativity bursting into life, Rosemary stimulates the psyche while tapping into the enormous riches of the creative, imaginal realm. Recharge your creative batteries, reconnect to your creative fire and allow the next part of your cycle to emerge. Imagine how someone else would approach your concerns creatively. What innovative changes would that person instigate?

An easy and powerful way to get your imagination working on any situation you want to explore is to ask the question, "what if?".

- *What if you imagined you are the creative idea you desire to bring to life?*
- *What would your creative endeavours taste, feel, smell, sound and look like?*
- *What motivates you to be creative?*
- *What are the creative breakthroughs you need to have?*

♥ Blossoming Heart Affirmation

I am the very essence of creation.

Rosewood Aniba roseodora

Receptive - Hindered

*All you need to do to receive guidance
is to ask for it and then listen.*
Sanaya Roman

 tree, heartwood and chips

 rose-like, woody, light

 6

Rosewood enables a greater receptivity to different kinds of awareness, sensory perceptions and energy streams that roam within the labyrinth of your unconscious mind.

Tuning you into the older, universally accumulated truths that waft back and forth across the psyche, Rosewood, with its light, warm aroma, accesses the eternal intuitiveness that rests deeply within the trunk of your own wise wood.

If you are feeling blocked in some area of your life, then seek interior guidance and make a request for what you need to experience in order to see the truth behind things.

* *Does some aspect of your life make you feel hindered?*
* *What question do you need to ask of your deeper, instinctual self?*
* *How can you benefit by tuning in to what you already know as true?*

♥ Blossoming Heart Affirmation

I am receptive to my interior guidance.

Sage Salvia officinalis

Wise - Unknowing

*Do not sacrifice upon the altar of your mind the
sacred wisdom that rises with each beat of your heart.*

Ken Carey

 herb, aerial plant parts

 herby

 3

Like echoes of ancient wisdom, Sage acknowledges a deeper, collective consciousness being woven within the rich tapestry of any spiritual quest. The strong, fresh, herbal fragrance of Sage takes you to your own source through the use of sacred ritual.

Meaningful rituals speak the language of your soul, providing a framework and focus for sacred work. Rituals celebrate rites of passage creating vast streams of possibility, drawing upon space, time and nature, symbolically representing what has been before and what is yet to emerge.

Sage brings one's entire self to a higher order, transcending and renewing while making a journey inward to a deeper place of knowing. There are many lessons and wisdoms learned along the path of life and it is important that you listen to and honour that inner wisdom. Live your life from your heart and know that your inner resources and wisdom will naturally appear.

* *What is it that you know?*
* *What are your favourite rituals that create
deepening in your life?*
* *What is the nature of your quest?*

♥ Blossoming Heart Affirmation

My heart and wisdom mind are one.

Sandalwood - East Indian Santalum album

Reflective - Entrenched

*It is looking at things for a long time that ripens
you and gives you a deeper understanding.*

Vincent van Gogh

> *tree, heartwood*
>
> *warm, woody, balsamic*
>
> *6*

The warm, spicy fragrance of Sandalwood offers a higher perspective from which to view your life.

Do you feel entrenched in the busyness of life? Is your energy being constantly dissipated as you run from moment to moment, leaving you emotionally drained and unable to have a clear view of the future? Then use Sandalwood to help you let go of being busy and embrace time to be.

When seeking an overview, guidance or wise council concerning a particular aspect of your life, take time out for quiet reflection. Imagine standing on the highest mountain where the view is clear and expansive. Sandalwood will support you in shifting you from your present point of view, to a different kind of viewing point.

Sandalwood has the ability to support the adrenal and kidney energies that can become out of balance through anxiety and frustration not being dealt with effectively.

Simplify, pare down, and take the time to have a short sabbatical from your life, your marriage, your job and your concerns, giving you time out to contemplate so that all nuances are clarified for clearer viewing.

- *What tools do you have that encourage contemplation?*
- *Do you need to address an issue in another way?*

♥ Blossoming Heart Affirmation

I look towards the far horizon.

Spearmint Mentha spicata

Invigorated - Weary

*Tell me what it is you plan to do
with your one wild and precious life.*
Mary Oliver

 herb, leaves

 fresh, sweet, minty, cool

🌢 *2*

Spearmint with its fresh, stimulating, minty, green fragrance, invigorates, strengthens and fosters your commitment to the catalystic and evolutionary process.

Your energy drives your body and it is your intention that drives your energy. The word intention comes from the Latin root, *intendre*, meaning to stretch toward something. There is a power that comes with setting an intention. Accomplishments are achieved with greater ease when your energy and your intention are truly aligned.

Feeling weary of body and mind? Are you being held back by your own annoying lethargy? Then use spearmint to wake up, keep moving, get excited, harness your energy, get your liver functioning and your mind into learning. Also eat nourishing foods that bring you fully into life.

- *What environments make you feel the most invigorated and bring out the best in you?*
- *What are you stretching toward at this time in your life?*

♥ Blossoming Heart Affirmation

My intention and my energy are aligned.

Spruce _Picea mariana_

Motivated - Defeated

_One does not discover new lands without consenting
to lose sight of the shore for a very long time._
Andre Gide

🌰 _tree, terminal branches_

2 _fresh, pine-like_

💧 _4_

When suffering lingers too long and defeat and exhaustion pervade all areas of your life, refreshing, aromatic Spruce descends deep into the unlimited energy reserves that lie dormant within your being.

Like the warmth of a radiant sun upon your face, Spruce activates the release of a healthy flow of energy from the adrenal glands to refresh and bring strength to each new day.

With defeat often comes a fatigue of body, mind and spirit that can be carried in your posture. To change how you feel you need to change your energy. Stretch out and consciously move your body away from any posture of defeat. Apply Spruce to the lumbar area of your back to support your adrenal glands.

Spruce encourages a broadening and opening to a sense of spaciousness within, a way of seeing your journey through life in a brand new way. Spruce adds a depth of insight previously unknown and has the capacity to shift you from feelings of defeat to feeling refreshed and motivated.

- _If you were to reflect upon your suffering and concerns differently, could you see your future being reshaped in a new way?_
- _What qualities of refreshment can you add to your life on a daily basis?_
- _What motivates you?_

♥ Blossoming Heart Affirmation

_Energy flows where my motivation goes.
Motivation goes where my energy flows._

Tea Tree Melaleuca alternifolia

Understanding - Intolerant

*Nothing worse could happen to one than
to be completely understood.*
C.G.Jung

 tree, leaves, twigs

warm, spicy

3

The spicy, bittersweet scent of Tea Tree promotes patience and understanding and assists in extending your tolerance when dealing with challenging situations. Intolerant behaviour will drop away when you have true empathy and a desire for resolution. Learn to manage your differences differently, speak collaboratively and bring others alongside of you. Go for win-win thinking!

For dialogue to be effective and fruitful it is necessary to listen well and the gift that follows is the one of understanding. Tea Tree brings the ability to naturally acknowledge and appreciate the other side of the picture and view the perspectives of others without feeling threatened.

Tea Tree will take you beyond any points of difference, raise your tolerance level and encourage you to see the bigger picture.

Tea Tree builds confidence and a strong sense of integrity that also helps to develop robust immunity and inner containment.

• *Where do you require greater tolerance in your life?*

• *Is there a current issue that needs to be resolved?*

♥ Blossoming Heart Affirmation

Patience, tolerance and genuine interest enhance my understanding.

Thyme Thymus vulgaris- ct linalol

Dynamic - Powerless

*Reverence is a natural aspect of authentic
empowerment because the soul revers all of life.*
Gary Zukov

💧 *herb, leaves, flowering tops*

🜂 *fresh, herby, warm, spicy,*

💧 *4*

Strong and fiery, Thyme activates a vital force for the positive use of willpower, strengthening resolve and assisting in the breaking of negative patterns or habits.

When the sun of the old order is setting and you need to re-orchestrate the patterns of your life, Thyme provides a fresh perspective with its powerfully radiating heat.

Thyme brings in a dynamic quality of energy that is needed by the physical body to maintain willpower, instilling a greater sense of fulfillment, empowerment and strong belief in oneself. Harness your own healing powers, access your strength, know that you are on track and that nothing will turn you away from any new resolve.

• *Is there a place in your life where you feel powerless?*

• *How would you describe your relationship to power?*

• *When are you at your most dynamic and radiating
a positive glow?*

♥ Blossoming Heart Affirmation

I am a powerhouse of energy.

Vetiver Vetiveria zizanioides

Assurance - Threatened

Every blade of grass has its own angel
that bends over it and whispers, grow, grow.
The Talmud

grass, roots

rich, woody, earthy, smoky,

2

When turning points in life challenge you to face your shadows, Vetiver, with its stabilizing tranquillity brings a quiet assurance, drawing you to the earth, offering support and strength as you reconcile the changes taking place.

If you are feeling threatened by the demands of your own soul for change, Vetiver will embrace, sustain and re-establish a balanced relationship between your heart, body and mind.

It is possible to change if you learn new ways and the musty, earthy quality of Vetiver lends itself to thoughtful consideration as you discard ways of relating that no longer serve you. In autumn, the trees drop their leaves shedding what is no longer needed. Then nature takes a quiet pause and waits for the recurring miracle of a new cycle of growth to emerge. You too, can also shed that which is no longer required and wait in the quiet stillness for new life to come forth.

In the velvety light of a new dawn, Vetiver holds you steady, increases your endurance and strengthens your heart so it can remain open to what is challenging.

- *Where in your life do you feel the most assured?*
- *Is there a part or a quality of your life*
  that you need to shed?

♥ Blossoming Heart Affirmation

My heart blossoms with quiet assurance.

Wintergreen Gaultheria procumbens

Productive - Inert

God gives us the nuts but he does not crack them.
Old German Proverb

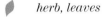

    herb, leaves

    sweet, minty, strong, cool

    1

When you are heavy with inertia and motivation evades you, Wintergreen, with its dynamic action, will push you toward greater productivity, refocus your goals and keep you on track.

Help to tip the scales in your favour and harness yourself for action. Use Wintergreen particularly when you have been procrastinating and putting off important tasks. Variety in your life will increase your productivity. Stop procrastinating now and get on with it! If you feel that your energy has been flagging and you need a boost to get moving again then Wintergreen is the oil for you.

- *In what situations do you become inert?*
- *How does your body feel when you are inert?*
- *What is the best way you know to call yourself to action?*
- *Is there someone in your life whom you can look toward for inspiration and motivation?*

♥ Blossoming Heart Affirmation

Productive variety is the spice of life.

113

Yarrow Achillea millefolium

Balanced - Erratic

*You become truly part of the world when you recognise
how its contradictions and its beauty live in you.*

Stephanie Dowrick

herb, flowering tops

green, herby, fresh, resinous

3

Yarrow, a sacred plant of ancient China, superbly represents the qualities of Yin and Yang, The outer stem of the plant is hard and strong - a Yang or masculine quality. The inner stem is filled with a soft substance - a Yin or feminine quality. Everything in the universe is a manifestation of these two opposite energies which attract and balance each other. To be effective we must have a balance of both masculine and feminine energy.

Yarrow stabilises polar opposites within the body and is useful during times of major life changes, when emotional equilibrium needs greater support.

Yarrow will bring balance when life is testing you on your weaknesses, your behaviour is erratic and you know you are behaving badly. Just as nature impressively romps between mayhem and order, recognise that your own rhythm is echoed here.

Learn how to maintain your balance in every situation without abandoning your integrity. Ask for clarity of vision so that your inner perspectives will match your external actions. Yarrow with its balancing action refines the senses, enhancing the power of your insights as well as your outer vision.

Change your pace. Dance wildly to the rhythm of a different kind of drum. Investigate various body therapies that will bring balance into your life such as good nutrition, chiropractic care or osteopathy, aromatherapy massage, acupuncture, pilates, yoga and kinesiology.

- *Are there some different routines you could incorporate into your daily life to centre yourself?*
- *What new perspective will bring balance into your life?*

♥ Blossoming Heart Affirmation

I am the balance point in my life.

Ylang Ylang Cananga odorata

Mindful - Angry

My religion is simple. My religion is kindness.
The Dalai Lama

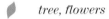

tree, flowers

floral, rich, heady, sweet, exotic, sensual

2

When you are angry and volatile as a storm cloud the striking intensity of Ylang Ylang matches the energy bound within. This exotic, sweet 'flower of flowers' softens attitudes, breaks old patterns and evokes flexibility.

Take up the challenge. Learn to recognize your inner resources, assets and life experiences to help you to construct a way through and beyond any residue of anger. Emotion is simply energy demanding motion. Explore and transform your anger and be mindful of how you are affecting others. Ylang Ylang harbours the capacity for growth and deepening of relationships. Mindful practice expresses itself in acts of kindness. Reflect on the kindnesses you share with others.

Modify your physical and mental state and embrace your emotional world from a place of compassionate distance. Focus on your breath and mindfully change your response. Consider where knots of anger may be located in your body. Mindfully apply Ylang Ylang over those parts to nourish and relax your body and mind. Learn to meditate. Practise walking meditation. Let there be peace in every step you take.

- *When you are angry how can it become a teacher, a gift?*
- *What specific area do you need to address in your life to move you away from any anger?*

♥ Blossoming Heart Affirmation

There is mindfulness in every step I take.

CHAPTER SEVEN

A Tale of Turkish Delights

Let holiness move in us so we may pay attention to its small voice and give ourselves fully with both hands.
Dawna Markova

A Tale of Turkish Delights

If it is true that the human spirit is indeed motivated through the heart allowing thinking and feeling to become eloquently expansive, then the following story illustrates this wonderfully.

I believe we call experiences to us at different times in our lives to recognise and heighten the strengths and divine purpose inherent in each of us. A few years ago our Turkish Aromatic Odyssey tour, brought together a delightful array of people from six different countries. Within hours of gathering in Istanbul for the commencement of the tour, this group developed a cohesiveness that Jim and I had never experienced so rapidly with previous tours. This group was born to journey together, to laugh and to enjoy!

Around the corner there may wait a new road or a secret gate.

J.R.R. Tolkein

Our last night in Istanbul found us in a boisterous seafood restaurant celebrating Hector's seventieth birthday. Hector was a lawyer and quietly refined. Earlier in the evening, he sashayed down the stairs into the hotel lobby, dressed in his purchases from The Grand Bazaar. A regal jalaba (caftan) with an embroidered felt hat sitting jauntily upon his head, brought cries of delight from the women in the group. They draped themselves around him on the divan for a photographic opportunity too good to miss. Photographed in the true style of a sultan with his harem, I think Hector was beginning to enjoy himself.

At the restaurant, Jim had managed to procure a birthday cake decorated in startling shades of iridescent green and pink which was exuberantly deposited in front of Hector by the grinning waiter. After much singing, dancing and hilarity it was time to retire as we were heading off just after dawn.

Overnight in Cappadoccia, we stayed in a cave house hotel in a tiny, remote village, complete with braying donkeys and a one thousand-year-old Byzantine monastery. The hotel was stunning.

Next morning Hector received a phone call from Australia informing him that his sister had passed away. She had been unwell for quite some time. Hector walked up through the village to a high point where he could continue his mobile phone conversation. As he was standing there on the hill with tears streaming down his face, a little girl, perhaps five or six years old came out through a wooden archway leading from her house. She came up to Hector and silently slipped her tiny hand in his and also began gently weeping.

She spoke no English, which didn't matter at all, for the language of the compassionate heart was fully present. Generosity of spirit in action needs no words. There they quietly stood in comforting communion.

In that moment, Hector decided not to return to Melbourne where the funeral was to be held. Instead, he and his wife Caroline asked me if I would be willing to hold a memorial service for his sister. I agreed, trusting that the right words would flow to honour the life of this woman whom I had never met.

We decided to conduct the service in four days time, when we arrived at our spa hotel on the Mediterranean. Two days later, while picking fragrant rose flowers under the early morning sun, in the Valley of the Roses, another member of our group, Jocelyn, received word that her father had passed away. This gentleman had also been suffering a long-term illness. We all spent some time in deep reflection for surely this was an uncanny coincidence. Surrounded by fields of beautiful Damask roses that symbolise divine love, a sense of belonging and a connection to the heart-centre, our own hearts swelled with a great empathy.

It is only with the heart that one can see rightly;
what is essential is invisible to the eye.
Antoine de Saint Exupery

The group was understandably subdued on the bus, as we meandered our way through the striking Taurus Mountains down to the coast. We found the perfect place to hold the ceremony, under a quaint pergola decorated with calico on the small private pier belonging to the hotel. The next morning as the sun was rising out of the turquoise sea we were all there, eighteen of us including our Turkish guide and our warm-hearted bus driver who did not speak English.

Somehow I did find the right words to say. We sang Amazing Grace and tossed rose petals into the water, reflecting quietly on the loved ones who are no longer with us. The wheel of life takes us around and back again to the simplest of things, ashes to ashes and dust to dust. Several months later we discovered that at the service in Melbourne for Hector's sister, the congregation also sang Amazing Grace. There is beauty and elegance in that kind of synchronicity.

What comes from the heart touches the heart.
Don Sibet

As I threw the last remaining rose petals into the sea, Hector dived into them for a final commemorative swim in honour of his sister.

For Jocelyn, the visit to the rose fields and the petals floating in the water would be etched in her memory forever. For Hector, his trip to Turkey, and particularly the rose ceremony, had been a highlight of his life. Quite a journey for the man who on arriving at our office to pay for the tour, introduced himself by saying, "I'm just coming along to carry the bags for my wife Caroline!".

How but in custom and ceremony are innocence and beauty born.

W.B. Yeats

When our hearts are open we draw the fullness of experience towards us and this wonderful group of people, collectively, instinctively, shared a loving time together. The last few days of the tour continued on in high frivolity, with much laughter, love and the finest of conversations. There is nothing quite like a ritual or ceremonial event to call us to a higher order of being.

CHAPTER EIGHT

Emotional Wellbeing to Soothe the Soul

Angels fly because they take themselves lightly.
Anonymous

Emotional Wellbeing to Soothe the Soul

There are times in life when we are not as resourceful in maintaining our emotional wellbeing as we would like to be. The heart, the body and the mind may need a little help if there is congestion in our energies.

We all know what stress feels like. It is well known that emotional stresses and strains have an effect on our physical body. What we think and feel can influence our health and it is unusual to fall ill when we are feeling on top of the world. Research shows that many medical complaints contain a strong emotional or psychological component. There are some who believe that that all disease has its origin in an unmet emotional need of some kind.

We easily recognise stress effects such as butterflies in the stomach before a presentation, a pounding heart when feeling afraid or a lack of appetite after a heated argument. Most of us have an area in the physical body that becomes vulnerable when we are tired, run down or emotionally stressed. Have you ever become unwell after a stressful experience? Consider which part of your body succumbs when you are under stress. Most people can respond readily to this question. And yet not all stress is bad, as not enough change and stimulation can also be a threat to our wellbeing. Balance is the key.

We are what we think. All that we are arises with our thoughts.
With our thoughts we make the world.

Buddha

Twenty years ago if someone had told me that reading a book could change your life I never would have believed it. When I first experienced kinesiology I was astounded by its efficacy in improving my wellbeing and in resolving some emotional stress I was experiencing. At the time I was beginning my life long journey into the study of complementary therapies and had begun working as an assistant in an acupuncture clinic. One day, **Touch for Health** written by Dr John Thie appeared at the clinic. From that instant, my life, as I live it today, began. It was one of those defining moments that totally change the direction in which you are travelling. Kinesiology as a modality really caught my attention. I began to study it in earnest and have arrived at my own ideas and philosophies some twenty-five years later. I have called this philosophy Aromatic Kinesiology.

My career has brought me wonderful rewards. I maintain a busy clinical practice, I travel the world teaching what I love and have extended that concept to taking people on tour to places of great beauty and aromatic interest. I feel blessed. And yet, marvellous as it is, there are times when I do feel stressed. Life is very busy and at times disorder reigns in spite of the best laid plans. I too, need to find the *time to be*. Time to embrace my own still point within.

When I first began studying kinesiology, I learned some very effective techniques for stress relief. They quickly rebalance the body's energies and get things flowing along again. I teach these techniques during seminars and combined with using essential oils they are very useful self-help tools. We don't always need to go the long route to get some help. If you can have something at your fingertips on a daily basis to keep you feeling centred, vibrant and alert you will be less likely to fall in a soggy, saggy heap when bigger stresses occur.

> *You cannot always control what goes on outside,*
> *but you can always control what goes on inside.*
> Wayne Dyer

Emotional Stress Relief

Activation of the emotional stress relief points is the most simple, effective and valuable of all these techniques. The points affect the blood circulation and are directly linked to other parts of the body and also the meridians. They are located at the frontal eminences, the bumps on the forehead, about one inch above the eyebrow. By touching these points lightly while thinking of a stressful situation or negative emotion, messages are sent to the brain via the nervous system to clear the stress and avoid a reactive response.

Holding these points works in two directions at once to reset the brain. Firstly, they serve to stabilise and calm the body. Once the body has reported that its internal processes are returning to normal, circulation is restored and blood is redirected to the cerebral cortex at the front of the brain. The returning blood supply switches our normal mental process back into gear so that we can think rationally again. We recover from being overwhelmed and move back into a more resourceful state of mind.

Holding the emotional stress relief points brings the gift of transforming our point of view about stress, improves our ability to cope and reduces the emotional charge that occurs because of the stress we are experiencing.

When you feel stressed, touching these points can make a surprising difference to how you feel and what you think. You can reprogram your response to stress and also clear the residue of earlier hurts and traumas.

Frequent use of the emotional stress relief points will enable you to better manage your body's response to stress. The effects of accumulated stress will be diminished, your health will be enhanced and your energies will flow along with greater ease. Often neck and shoulder tightness, stomach upsets, jaw tension, headaches, bad moods and low energy will simply drop away. The emotional stress relief points lead you to that quiet place inside where you can experience *time to be*.

Interestingly, when we receive a shock or a surprise often our hand will automatically go to our forehead. I call the emotional stress relief points, the "Oh no! What am I going to do now?" points. Holding our head can bring relief in a very short space of time so that we can think more clearly.

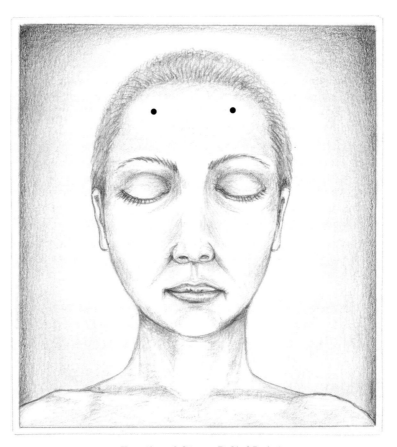

Emotional Stress Relief Points

126

How to balance the Emotional Stress Relief points.

- *Sit comfortably in a chair.*

- *Think about the emotion or situation that is causing you to be stressed.*

- *Place your fingertips on the neuro-vascular points on your forehead.*

- *Slightly stretch the skin outwards.*

- *Lightly hold these points for at least three minutes or longer if you prefer.*

- *Breathe deeply for a few moments.*

- *You will begin to think more clearly as the blood returns to your forebrain.*

- *After a short while you will feel tiny pulses synchronising under your fingertips.*

- *This signals that the process is complete for now.*

A variation of the above is to place one hand across your forehead and the other on the back of your head. This brings balance to the front and back of the brain. To have your head held by another person in this manner, is very relaxing.

Either of the above techniques can be used when you want to enhance a positive aspect of your life or to emphasise an affirmation you are saying regularly. Both direct your thinking to produce positive results. Combined with essential oils and the Essential Oil Reflections, aromatic anchoring adds another dimension to this simple, yet highly effective technique.

However, it is useful to know that in a crisis, it does not matter how you do this procedure just as long as you remember to hold the points!

As well as holding your emotional stress relief points regularly, the following stress soothers will help you to bring more calm into your life when things seem a bit hectic. Soaking in the bath with a few drops of your chosen essential oil and holding the points can be a great way to let go of a stressful day.

Subtle Stress Soothers

- *Breathe deeply.*
- *Exercise regularly, stretch your body, do shoulder scrunches.*
- *Read the Essential Oil Reflections.*
- *Soak in an aromatic bath.*
- *Take power naps.*
- *Create affirmations for your life.*
- *Hug a friend, hug a tree, hug yourself.*
- *Enjoy an aromatherapy massage.*
- *Listen to music.*
- *Balance your energies using kinesiology.*
- *Take time out with friends.*
- *Drink refreshing herbal teas and pure water.*
- *Get a good nights sleep.*
- *Eat foods that are compatible with your body.*
- *Vaporise essential oils to enhance your mood and environment.*

The ordinary acts we practice everyday at home are of more importance to the soul than their simplicity might suggest.
Thomas Moore

Pause for a Blossoming Heart

- *What are the best ways you know to relieve your stress?*
- *When was the last time you truly rested?*
- *How do you create time to be?*
- *Practise holding your emotional stress relief points and notice the effects.*

Daniel's story

Daniel came for an appointment because his constant angry outbursts and aggressive behaviour were disrupting his family life. On assessing Daniel's energy system it became apparent that his liver and spleen meridians were congested. After holding his emotional stress relief points for about ten minutes Daniel finally felt comfortable enough to tell me that he had been feeling picked on by his siblings at home.

We talked about some of his behaviours and what he himself could do differently. I blended two drops of Vetiver essential oil in a carrier oil to rub over his chest and made a Bush Flower Essence remedy to reduce his stress response. On the Aromatic Emotional Barometer Vetiver's associated words are Assurance/Threatened. Daniel needed to find a way to develop his self-assurance. The more he felt threatened then the more disruptive his behaviour would become.

Towards the close of the session and while I continued to hold his emotional stress relief points, I asked Daniel to see himself at home playing happily with his brothers. His face was quite flushed from emotionally and energetically working so hard at arriving at a workable solution.

His mother reported the following week that the change in Daniel was remarkable. For a period of time he continued to apply Vetiver over his chest and held his own emotional stress relief points whenever he felt the need.

Daniel is only eight years old but old enough to recognise that he needed help. It was *he* who actually requested the appointment. With all the members of his family consulting with me over a number of years for their emotional care and wellbeing, Daniel knew where he could go to receive some help to feel better. Age is no barrier and children respond beautifully to this simple technique.

CHAPTER NINE

Meridians and Emotional Expressions

Ten thousand flowers in spring, the moon in autumn,
a cool breeze in summer, snow in winter. If your
mind is not clouded by unnecessary things,
this is the best season of your life.
Wu-Men

Meridians and Emotional Expressions

Everybody has an energy circulation. To maintain good health it is essential for your body's energy, as well as the blood, to circulate in a continuous and unobstructed manner. The pathways, through which this energy flows, are called meridians. The meridians can be likened to a vast distribution network moving energy into, through and out of your body via a complex system of energy points.

The energy that flows along the meridians is called chi or prana. In Traditional Chinese Medicine (TCM), the flow of this vital energy around the body is seen as imperative to your health and wellbeing. The meridians can also be considered as the major arteries through which the life force acts on the etheric body. The clarity and proper functioning of the meridians is essential to the physical, mental, emotional and spiritual bodies.

The meridians, and their acupuncture points, are like signposts on the map of the body. They indicate where imbalances lie, often manifesting as physical and emotional disorders in the body.

The meridians could also be viewed as a pathway for a particular stream of consciousness. All physical conditions or imbalances make a statement about the state of a person's consciousness. Each meridian is related to a specific organ and muscle and many things influence the subtle way in which they work. Your diet, posture, thoughts, feelings, habits and the way you function can have a positive or negative effect on your meridian system. The consciousness or the awareness of a person may therefore, determine the patterns of unwellness that develop in the physical body.

Emotional Suppression

Emotional blockages have a strong potential to create imbalances in our energies as they can be locked away in our subconscious. Undigested events can show up later in life as unwellness, affecting you physically, emotionally and spiritually. Emotions are a normal response to stimuli from the external environment. Within normal limits, emotions cause no real problem in the body. However, it is when our emotions become overpowering and uncontrollable, overwhelming us with their constant presence that problems can occur. Unresolved emotional issues and mismanaged emotional states can cause serious disruption to the chi and open the door to ill health.

Suppression of feelings such as love, worry, grief, fear and anger, can lead to an imbalance in the meridians and the related muscles and organs. Emotional suppression may be a conscious or an unconscious decision that you make. It is not the intensity of an emotion but rather the extended duration of an emotional state that can rob you of your energy and vitality.

Over the years, while working with thousands of clients and students, I have found that specific essential oils consistently bring balance to the meridians when muscle testing the energy of the body. Clients report that they feel better, enjoy a more even temperament, are easier of mind and heart and have greater vitality.

> *Looking for and enjoying beauty is a way to nourish the soul.*
> Mathew Fox

Energy testing an indicator muscle that is associated with a corresponding organ, gland or meridian, can determine a state of stress or imbalance. For example, pectoralis major clavicular is a muscle linked with the stomach meridian. As well as activating digestion it is also connected to our emotional world. Peppermint essential oil is commonly used for digestive upsets. It also stimulates the function of the stomach meridian and enhances the digestion of new ideas.

During consultations I trace the meridians with essential oils, place aromatic blends over acupuncture points and various meridian reflex points located on the body and the head. Essential oils have the capacity to act as catalysts to connect the points of energy along the meridians.

Heart Blossom Points

On each meridian there is a stress collection area. By placing an essential oil over a certain acupuncture point and rubbing it firmly for a short time, emotional congestion begins to be released, enhancing the energy flowing through the meridian. I call these Heart Blossom Points. They are the quiet achievers for clearing emotional turmoil and balancing the energies in the meridians. The Heart Blossom Points settle the emotional heart.

Activate the Heart Blossom Points to:
• *Feel more energized more often.*

• *Think constructively and clearly.*

• *See the world around you more brightly.*

• *Be more resourceful and take action.*

• *Move away from anxiety and worry.*

• *Hear more positive internal dialogue.*

• *Be a shining light and inspiration to others.*

Once you have identified which meridian is out of balance and you become consciously aware of how you are feeling, you will ease emotional tension very swiftly. Using essential oils will create a better flow of energy through the meridian pathways, heightening your ability to make positive changes. Nothing gets your attention faster than when you are unwell, in pain or emotionally overwhelmed. The Heart Blossom Points offer a simple solution that will help you to reduce your stress and feel more at ease. The rhythm of the fragrances will also put you back in touch with your own inner beauty.

Learning the Language of the Meridians

One of life's most interesting challenges is to understand the way we 'tick'. This gives us greater options for knowing ourselves and changing our behaviours. The challenge around the language of the meridians is its unfamiliarity. It takes time to recognise the distinctions of the meridian emotional expressions. Gradually, you will learn to become familiar with observing the unfamiliar. Once you integrate the correlation between the meridian imbalances and how your body is feeling, the more confident you will be in reducing stress.

The body is simply intricate and intricately simple.
George Goodheart

The concept of the meridians presented on the following pages is simple. However, the healing principles of Aromatic Kinesiology and TCM, are somewhat more complex. The meridian emotional correlations and some physical indications are offered for your interest, to enable you to reprogram your responses to stress in an easy and effective way.

Carefully read over the meridian descriptions to identify any of the emotional expressions that may apply to you. If you are familiar with kinesiology or energy testing of the body you can use that method to determine the meridian and essential oil.

Each person carries his own doctor within.
Albert Schweitzer

You can influence your meridian energies successfully using essential oils on a daily basis. When you are feeling a bit down and emotionally congested choose an essential oil that you instinctively feel will help you redirect your energies. You can reduce the effects of emotional imbalances in your meridians and develop greater vitality. It takes but a moment to enhance your energies in this way.

How to balance the Heart Blossom Points with Essential Oils

1. Identify the meridian that is out of balance.

2. Make a single blend or use a combination of a few of the essential oils relative to the meridian qualities you would like to change.

3. Locate the Heart Blossom Points as seen in the diagram on the relevant meridian page. *All points are bilateral except for the Conception and Governing vessel points.*

4. Place a drop of your aromatic blend over the Heart Blossom Point and rub the area firmly for about thirty seconds or longer.

5. To expand your frame of reference further, refer to the Essential Oil Reflections and The Aromatic Emotional Barometer.

At least three times a day, or whenever you feel your energy drop, rub the relevant Heart Blossom Points to help your energies stay on track and give yourself a boost.

Don't be too concerned whether you have located the meridian point exactly. Massaging the area with three fingers will ensure that you do activate the point.

You may also:-

a) Place the chosen essential oil in a vaporiser to influence your environment so that your mind will continue to be refreshed and balanced.

b) Apply a few drops of the aromatic blend to any area of your body where you sense you are carrying stress and tension.

c) Apply the aromatic blend to the feet, wrists and the back of the head. This is particularly useful to do just before you go to sleep, as your night-mind dissipates stress and restores balance to the energies.

d) Apply the aromatic blend with a brisk friction massage either side of the length of your spine. This will help to clear stagnant energies from your body.

After a few days you can use the remainder of the blended essential oil in a warm, relaxing, aromatic bath.

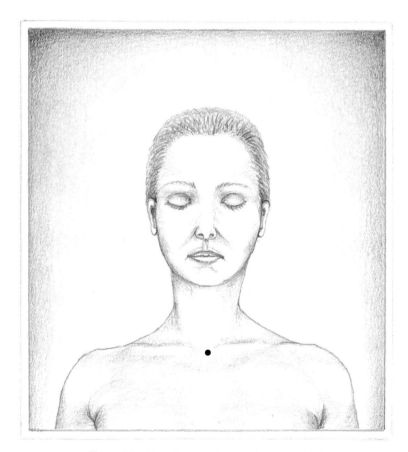

Heart Blossom Point - Conception Vessel 21

Conception Vessel – Brain

Essential Oils

- Basil
- Eucalyptus
- Grapefruit
- Lemongrass
- Rosemary
- Peppermint

Balanced emotional expression

- Sets achievable goals
- Balanced pursuit of objectives
- Conception of new ideas
- High spirits
- Focused
- Connected to the life path
- Serene
- Clear thinking
- Emotional presence
- Speaks with authority
- Comfortable with success

Imbalanced emotional expression

- Intense
- Consumed by goals
- Obsessive
- Workaholic
- Depression
- Mania
- Driven
- Unable to meet challenges
- Wounded inner child
- Perfectionist
- Unrealistic expectations
- Agitated
- Relentless

Conception Vessel is a reservoir or storehouse for the Yin meridians. It houses the feminine energy of being.

If there is too much stress in the Yin meridians there will not be enough energy available to support the tasks they need to do. Therefore, they will draw energy from Conception Vessel. It may cause you to feel overwhelmed, confused and disconnected until the reservoir of energy is replenished.

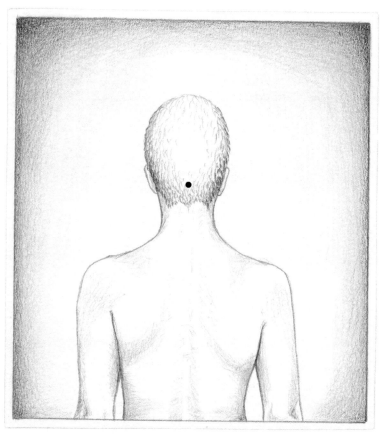

Heart Blossom Point - Governing Vessel 16

Governing Vessel - Nervous System

Essential Oils
- German Chamomile
- Frankincense
- Geranium
- Lemon
- Rosewood
- Spearmint

Balanced emotional expression
- Strong will power
- Regulated energy
- Positive interior guidance
- Intuitive hearing
- Inner authority
- Clear perception
- Connected to inner light
- Strong back bone
- Registers environmental influences
- Finely attuned to the subtle energies
- Able to give and receive support easily
- High trust in life's processes

Imbalanced emotional expression
- Lack of willpower
- Stubborn
- Overbearing
- Vacillating energy
- Selective hearing
- Shut off from the inner voice
- Fatigue
- Indifference
- Burdened
- Over-sensitive to changes in environment
- Recurrent negative habits
- Addictions
- Unable to see clearly with the inner eye
- Feels unsupported
- Does not trust easily

Governing Vessel is a reservoir or storehouse for the Yang meridians. It houses the masculine energy of doing.

If there is too much stress in the Yang meridians there will not be enough energy available to support the tasks they need to do. Therefore, they will draw energy from Governing Vessel. This may cause you to feel burdened and exhausted until the reservoir of energy is replenished.

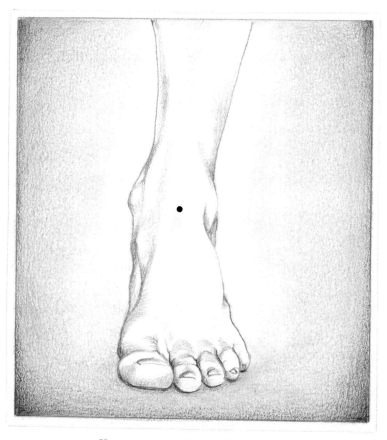

Heart Blossom Point - Stomach 41

Stomach Meridian - Yang

Essential Oils
- Aniseed Myrtle
- Fennel
- Ginger
- Lavender
- Marjoram
- Peppermint

Balanced emotional expression
- Socially graceful
- Well-organised
- Co-ordinated
- Able to see projects through
- Strong leadership ability
- Positive determination
- Good rhythm
- Sticks at things
- Self-nurturing
- Stable
- Productive
- Moderate
- Adaptable
- Well-prepared
- Has faith
- Satisfied
- Relaxed
- Proud of one's achievements
- Affectionate
- Calm
- Self-reliant

Imbalanced emotional expression
- Disorganized
- Clutter
- Incompletions
- Dissipated energy
- Poor judgement
- Insecure
- Inability to nurture oneself
- Craves sympathy
- Feels deprived
- Dissatisfied
- Emotional worries
- Resists change
- Churning inside
- Dependent
- Self doubt
- Often disappointed

Physical indications of imbalance
- Eczema
- Arthritis
- Rashes
- Sinusitis
- Asthma
- Toxic bowel
- Insomnia
- Neck and shoulder tension
- Bed wetting
- Hiatus hernia
- Food reflux
- Bad breath
- Acid digestion
- Morning sickness
- Hayfever
- Stomach ulcers
- Gas
- Burping
- Post nasal drip
- Colic
- Wide swings of energy

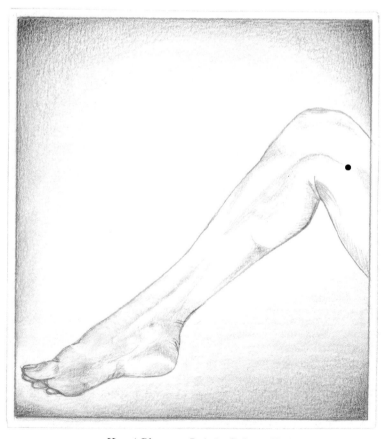

Heart Blossom Point - Spleen 10

Spleen Meridian - Yin

Essential Oils
- Benzoin
- Geranium
- Orange
- Rosemary
- Sandalwood
- Vetiver

Balanced emotional expression
- Responsible
- Good humour
- High spirited
- Fully present
- Grounded
- Practical
- Strong vitality
- Lively demeanor
- Receptive
- Balanced empathy
- Thoughtful
- Caring
- Creative
- Supportive
- Balanced nurturing of others
- Stable
- Centred
- Life feels sweet
- Ability to hold steady
- Even distribution of energy

Imbalanced emotional expression
- Daydreamer
- Vagueness
- Living in a fantasy world
- Depression
- No sense of humour
- Irresponsible
- Unstable
- Scattered
- Escapist tendencies
- Needy
- Self-denial
- Hides feelings
- Ungrounded
- Obsessive
- Selfish
- Tired
- Restless sleeper
- Confusion
- Inability to concentrate
- Rescuer personality type
- Over-protective
- Worrier
- Alienated
- Sensitive to disapproval
- Cynical
- Obsessive fixations
- Feels rejected
- Touch of the martyr

Physical indications of imbalance
- Disturbance in sweating mechanism
- Middle ear infections
- Food allergies
- Low blood sugar
- Too frequent urination
- Inability to heal
- Fatigue
- Sensitivity to gluten
- Fluid retention
- Inadequate lymph drainage
- Obesity
- Yeast sensitivity
- Diabetes
- Poor fat digestion
- Craves sweet foods
- Improper fat distribution around the waist (especially in men)

Heart Blossom Point - Heart 8

Heart Meridian - Yin

Essential Oils
- Cistus
- Jasmine
- Melissa
- Neroli
- Palmrosa
- Rose

Balanced emotional expression
- Sharp thinking
- Sense of belonging
- Feels prosperous
- Community minded
- Good memory
- Joyful
- Thoughtful of others
- Visionary
- Feels at one with all
- Ability to plan ahead
- Passionate
- Connected to the rhythm of life
- Confident
- Clear insight
- Compassionate
- Influential
- Loving
- Secure
- Warm-hearted

Imbalanced emotional expression
- Separate
- Inconsiderate
- Lack of joy
- Clouded thinking
- Lack of vision
- Feels poor
- Lonely
- Depression
- Anxiety
- Uneasiness
- Affected by shock
- Low self-esteem
- Shy
- Agitated
- Lack of self-love
- Feels unworthy
- Forgetful
- Manic
- Lack of confidence
- Insecure
- Forgiveness issues

Physical indications of imbalance
- Palpitations
- Dizziness
- Shoulder or chest pains
- Bleeding gums
- High or low blood pressure
- Poor circulation
- Hardening of arteries
- Poor memory
- Heart attacks
- Does not like the heat
- Insomnia

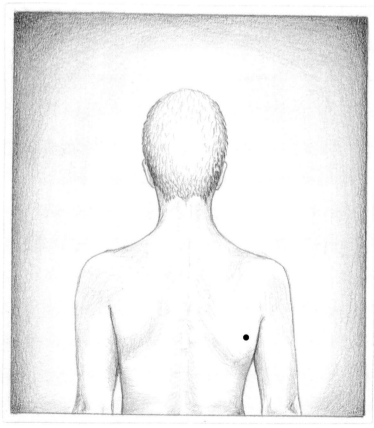

Heart Blossom Point - Small Intestine 11

Small Intestine Meridian - Yang

Essential Oils
- Cinnamon
- Clove bud
- Elemi
- Ginger
- Marjoram
- Rosewood

Balanced emotional expression
- Calm
- Courageous
- Confident
- Good listener
- Discerning
- Takes notice of inner guidance
- Decisive
- Wise
- Commitment comes easily
- Able to elicit co-operation from others
- Able to nurture oneself
- Able to assimilate nourishment physically, emotionally, mentally and spiritually

Imbalanced emotional expression
- Nervous
- Cowardly
- Gullible
- Distorted thinking
- Critical
- Mental confusion
- Unable to face fears
- Irritable
- Always agitated
- Highly strung
- Sadness
- Inability to make decisions
- Poor judgement
- Restless
- Feels unappreciated
- Over committed
- Lack of discernment
- Exhausted
- Sorrowful
- Internalizes thinking and feeling

Physical indications of imbalance
- Mouth ulcers
- Coated or cracked tongue
- Dull brittle hair
- Cold sores
- Constipation
- Diarrhoea
- Pre-menstrual tension
- Herpes
- Abdominal bloating
- Dark circles under eyes
- Pimples over cheekbones
- Hearing problems
- Frozen shoulder
- Indigestion

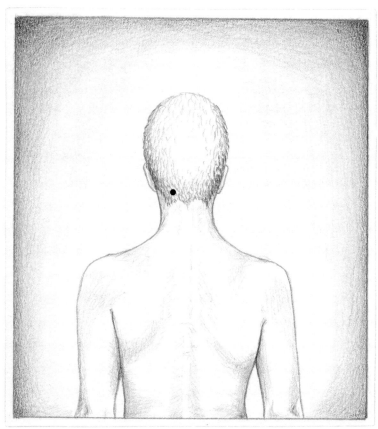

Heart Blossom Point - Bladder 10

Bladder Meridian - Yang

Essential Oils
- Bergamot
- Cedarwood
- Cypress
- Geranium
- Juniper
- Thyme

Balanced emotional expression
- Able to release harmful emotions
- Sure of oneself
- Resourceful
- In control of one's emotions
- Connected to the rhythms of life
- Definite
- Adaptable
- Peaceful
- Attuned to inner direction
- Reflective
- Resolute
- Courageous
- Confident
- Sets strong boundaries

Imbalanced emotional expression
- Weary
- Complaining
- Hardened
- Deep depression
- Storage of toxic emotions
- Explosive emotional outbursts
- Overly cautious
- Poor judgement about when to take action
- Erratic thinking
- Crying spells
- Suspicious nature
- Over-sensitive
- Fearful
- Burnt-out
- Exhausted
- Restless
- Impatient
- Frustrated

Physical indications of imbalance
- Bladder infections
- Cystitis
- Polyuria
- Urine retention
- Prostate symptoms
- Bacterial infection of uterine tract
- Muscle tension in the back, buttocks, tight hamstrings and calf muscles
- Sciatica
- Bedwetting

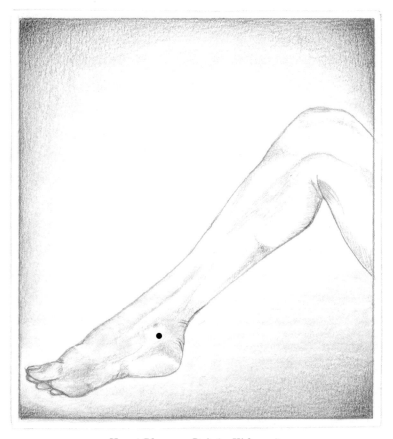

Heart Blossom Point - Kidney 5

Kidney Meridian - Yin

Essential Oils
- Cedarwood
- Clary Sage
- Geranium
- Ginger
- Sandalwood
- Spruce

Balanced emotional expression
- Positive
- Happy outlook
- Discerning
- Psychic awareness
- Grounded
- Consolidating
- Refined emotions
- Good reserves of energy or chi
- Alert
- Elegant
- Responsive
- Secure
- Strong willpower
- Able to endure and sustain
- Determined
- Loyal
- Decisive

Imbalanced emotional expression
- Anxiety
- Depression
- Neurotic
- Over-emotional
- Insecure
- Wavering energy levels
- Fear of failure
- Hatred
- Complains a lot
- Depleted
- Fearful
- Apprehensive
- Insensitive
- Unresponsive emotionally
- Tendency to withdraw and retreat
- Careless
- Cold inside
- Reckless
- Superstitious
- Holds on to old emotional patterns
- Narcissistic
- Panic attacks
- Lack of willpower
- Overwhelmed

Physical indications of imbalance
- Burning feet
- Leg pains
- Low back pain
- Fear of the dark
- Milky urine
- Armpit and foot odour
- Pigeon-toes
- 5pm fatigue
- Low/high blood pressure
- Bed-wetting
- Skin problems
- Facial oedema
- Craves salty foods
- Sweaty palms and feet
- Dark circles under eyes
- Low energy
- Sensitive to the cold
- Inability to relax
- Dull lifeless hair

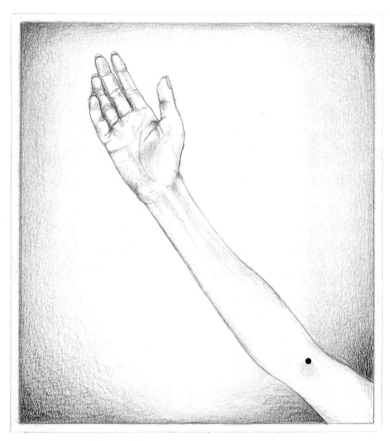

Heart Blossom Point - Pericardium 3

Pericardium Meridian - Yin
– Circulation and Hormones

Essential Oils
- Clary Sage
- Jasmine
- Rose
- Sage
- Yarrow
- Ylang Ylang

Balanced emotional expression
- Emotionally secure
- Sturdy emotional reserves
- Strong foundation of energy
- Able to defend oneself
- Enthusiastic
- Harmonious
- Warm
- Protected
- Well-integrated
- Relaxed
- Calm
- Charismatic
- Generous
- Protects the heart from emotional pressure

Imbalanced emotional expression
- Insecure
- Feels defenceless
- Emotions debilitating
- Defensive
- Despairing
- Gloomy
- Withdrawal required to recover from strong emotional outbursts
- Surrenders to illness easily
- Stubborn
- Jealous

Physical indications of imbalance

Female
- Pre-menstrual tension
- Bloating
- Anxiety
- Depression
- Weight gain
- Cravings
- Breast tenderness
- Fatigue
- Irritability
- Forgetfulness
- Headaches
- Menstrual cramps
- Menopausal symptoms

Male
- Prostate symptoms
- Impotence
- Diabetes
- Heart disease
- Insufficient skeletal muscle

General
- Tight diaphram
- Insomnia
- Exhaustion
- Heart palpitations
- Sore elbow
- Forearm pain

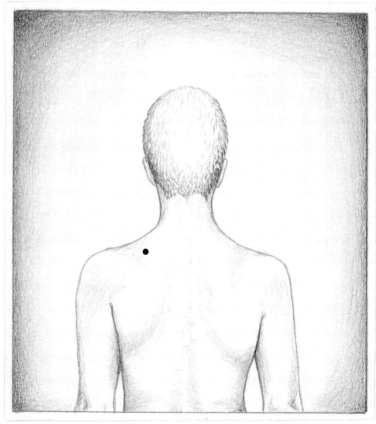

Heart Blossom Point - Triple Warmer 15

Triple Warmer Meridian - Yang – Thyroid, adrenals, temperature control

Essential Oils
- Angelica
- Geranium
- Lemongrass
- Nutmeg
- Patchouli
- Sandalwood

Balanced emotional expression
- Strong vitality
- Centred
- Focused
- Sound reasoning faculties
- Ethical
- Honourable
- High principles
- Grounded
- Discerning
- Regulated metabolism

Imbalanced emotional expression
- Poor reasoning faculties
- Lack of commonsense
- Flighty
- Short attention span
- Lazy
- Fatigue
- Sluggish thinking
- Fragmented
- Unfocused
- Lack of assimilation of nourishment
- Hopeless
- Panic
- Overwhelm
- Burnout
- Panic
- Hysteria
- Frenzied activity

Physical indications of imbalance
- Morning fatigue
- Swollen eyelids
- Constipation
- Very dry or oily skin
- Sugar cravings
- Depression
- Cold intolerance
- Low libido
- Weight problems
- High body temperature
- Rapid pulse
- Bulging eyes
- Inability to concentrate
- Cries easily.
- Acute menopausal symptoms
- Skin pigmentation
- Low or high blood pressure
- Allergies
- Fatigue
- Muscle weakness
- Low blood sugar
- Lower back pain
- Prone to infections
- Shoulder, arm, or wrist pain
- Earache

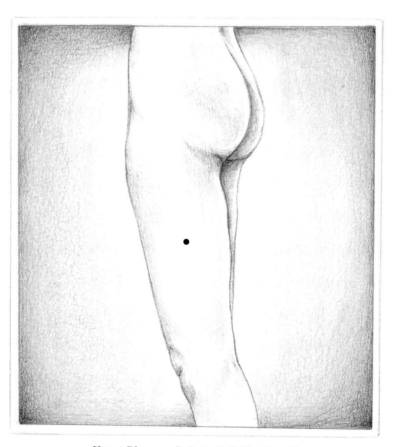

Heart Blossom Point - Gall Bladder 31

Gall Bladder Meridian - Yang

Essential Oils
- Basil
- Grapefruit
- Lemon
- Orange
- Rosemary
- Peppermint

Balanced emotional expression
- Decisive
- Rational thinking
- Orderly
- Good observation skills
- Well organized
- Methodical
- Purposeful
- Logical thought
- Ability to sort and break down information
- Resolute
- Sound judgement
- Wise decisions
- Motivated
- Assertive
- Powerful
- Accountable
- Purposeful
- Able to stand up for what you believe in

Imbalanced emotional expression
- Cunning
- Manipulative
- Unreasonable
- Jealous
- Bitter
- Illogical
- Indecisive
- Poor powers of observation
- Resentment
- Frustration
- Aggression
- Domineering
- Unexpressed anger
- Boredom
- Uninterested in one's appearance
- Can't be bothered

Physical indications of imbalance
- Pre-menstrual tension
- Gallstones
- Pale hard stools
- Fat intolerance
- Flatulence
- Nausea
- Fatigue
- Headaches
- Sleepiness after eating fats
- Skin problems
- Yellowish tinge to the skin
- Constipation
- Bitter taste in mouth
- Stiff neck and shoulder muscles

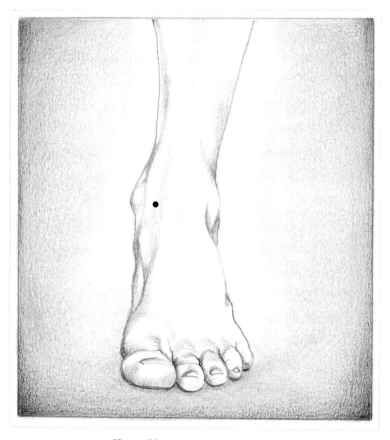

Heart Blossom Point - Liver 4

Liver Meridian - Yin

Essential Oils
- Basil
- Everlasting
- Lime
- Rosemary
- Spearmint
- Wintergreen

Balanced emotional expression
- Filter for the emotions
- Resilient
- Giving
- Loving
- Feels secure
- Able to create and bring ideas to fruition
- Superb planning skills
- Inspirational
- Calm under pressure
- Handles stress well
- Balanced ambition and drive
- Flexible
- Energetic
- Enthusiastic
- Assertive
- Wise determination
- Excellent strategist
- Contented
- Responsible

Imbalanced emotional expression
- Anger
- Irritability
- Moodiness
- Shouting
- Spiteful
- Rigid
- Miserly
- Unable to plan
- Lack of organization
- Unable to carry through ideas
- Grumpy
- Easily stressed
- Over-emphasis on being in control
- Frustration
- Furious
- Emotional suppression
- Aggressive
- Impatient
- Inflexible
- Lack of vision for the future
- Vengeful
- Hostile
- Feels toxic emotionally and physically
- Arrogant
- Opinionated
- Filled with rage
- Self-righteous
- Indignation
- Depression

Physical indications of imbalance
- Breast tenderness
- Irregular and painful periods
- Haemorrhoids
- Varicose veins
- Gout
- Uterine fibroids
- Swelling in legs and abdomen
- Excessive blood clotting
- Abnormal bleeding
- Cellulite
- Hepatitis
- Headaches
- Bad breath
- Constipation
- Skin problems
- Weak nails
- Coated tongue

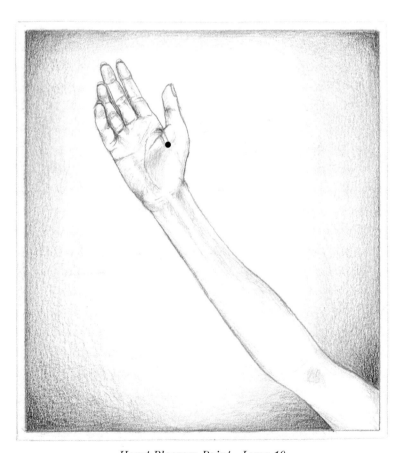

Heart Blossom Point - Lung 10

Lung Meridian - Yin

Essential Oils
- Eucalyptus
- Kunzea
- Myrtle
- Pine
- Ravensara
- Thyme

Balanced emotional expression
- Knows one's place in the scheme of things
- Positive thinking
- Strong leadership ability
- Fine integrity
- Thoughtful in speaking
- Integrated
- Cheerful
- Impeccable sense of knowing when and how to act
- Fully present
- Attentive
- Able to release old belief patterns and habits
- Powerful
- Strongly connected to the rhythm of the breath

Imbalanced emotional expression
- Daydreaming
- Can never get it right
- Poor listening ability
- Fidgety
- Fast talking
- Incessant trivial speech
- Procrastination
- Sorrow
- Negative thinking
- Rebellious
- Sadness
- Stuck in loss and grief
- Remote
- Apathetic
- Powerless
- Victim consciousness
- Boredom
- Lack of self-control
- Think the world owes them something
- Depressed
- Intolerant
- Regretful
- Shows contempt

Physical indications of imbalance
- Breathing irregularities
- Asthma
- Shortness of breath with exercise
- Rapid pulse
- Bad breath
- Chronic cough
- Throat problems
- Excess mucus
- Sinusitis
- Dry skin
- Very pale complexion

大腸經

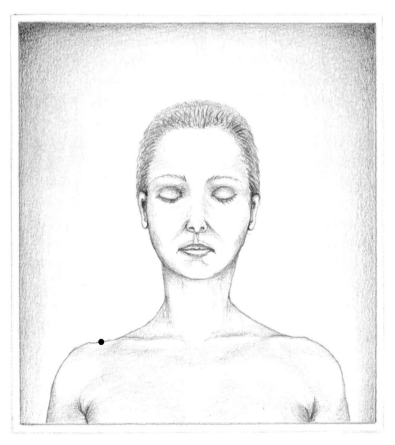

Heart Blossom Point - Large Intestine 16

Large Intestine Meridian - Yang

Essential Oils
- Clove Bud
- Fennel
- Marjoram
- Neroli
- Palmarosa
- Tea Tree

Balanced emotional expression
- Able to harvest the fruits of one's labours
- Substantial
- Robust
- Lack of attachment to non-essential things
- Courage
- Determined
- Able to set clear boundaries
- Reflective
- Strong self-worth
- Able to process and work through emotional issues
- Optimistic
- Enthusiastic
- Effective communication skills

Imbalanced emotional expression
- Regretful
- Withholding
- Inability to let go
- Sighs a lot
- Guilt-ridden
- Melancholy
- Lack of forgiveness
- Cynical
- Constricted
- Clingy
- Poor self-image
- Vulnerable
- Neurotic
- Anal-retentive
- Pessimistic
- Disappointment
- Lack of completion
- Denial
- Emotional holding patterns
- Remorse
- Depressed
- Perfectionist
- Psychic and emotional clutter

Physical indications of imbalance
- Constipation
- Diarrhoea
- Odiferous stools
- Itchy anus
- Arthritis
- Liver and kidney congestion
- Bad breath
- Body odour
- Tooth decay
- Herpes
- Haemorrhoids
- Burning tongue
- Cracks at corner of mouth
- Nose bleeds
- Back pain
- Worms
- Night cramps
- Cellulite
- Diverticulitis
- Dry, flaky skin

CHAPTER TEN

Rose Meditation for a Blossoming Heart

*From bliss indeed, all beings originate, by bliss they are
sustained, towards bliss they move, into it they merge.*
The Upanishads

Rose Meditation for a Blossoming Heart

Development and change are fundamental laws of life and are reflected in the processes of nature and in the journey of the human soul. Images of open flowers have been universally used as symbols of spiritual renaissance. Visualising the transformation of the closed bud of a flower to a fully opened bloom is both inspiring and evocative. Creative visualization can be used in conjunction with aromatic anchoring to create wellbeing, reinforce positive emotions and help to keep your energies vibrant and clear.

Use the Rose Meditation when you are ready to create an opening or a shift in your life. You may be experiencing a challenge, have a sense of feeling stuck and unable to see your next step. Perhaps you feel shut down, emotionally unavailable and you need to discover a new rhythm in your heart. Or you may simply wish to create new options and expand or enhance a situation in your life. The rose visualization is a great tool to use when you are in a time of transition and is a very powerful resource for change.

When the heart is ready the light enters it.
Flower A. Newhouse

Place a drop of rose oil on a tissue to inhale while doing the visualization...Be in a comfortable and relaxed position...Take a moment to pay attention to the beautiful wisdom of your breath...in breath...out breath...Inhale the rose oil through your nose and breathe out through your mouth, as if you were gently blowing out a candle...Notice how lightly effortlessly your breaths flow into one another...In breath...out breath...in breath...out breath.

Imagine a closed rosebud...Visualize the stem, the leaves and the bud itself...It is green in appearance as the sepals are closed...At the topmost point there is a pink tip...Visualize this as vividly as possible, keeping the image at the centre of your conscious mind...As you watch, you gradually become aware that a minuscule movement is taking place... The sepals begin to pull apart as their points turn outwards, enabling you to see the closed dusky pink petals...The sepals slowly move further apart ... Now you can see the bud-shaped petals of a beautiful delicate rose...Then the petals begin to unfold... The bud continues to expand slowly until the radiant rose is revealed bursting with fragrant beauty and you admire it with smiling delight.

As you inhale the rose essential oil...Imagine you are breathing in the scent of a softly fragrant rose ... Inhale its perfume, so delicate, sweet and pleasing to all of the senses...The rose's tender fragrance rises around you filling you with the essence of all that you love... awakening a symphony of fragrant celebration ... As you breathe in the scent with pleasure, the perfume wafts through you and around your being...Energizing you where you need to feel energized and soothing you where you need to feel soothed.

Now visualize the entire rose bush and imagine the life force rising up from the roots to the beautiful, glorious rose...Focus on the flower...Contemplate for a moment this wondrous miracle of nature, vital with its pulsating lifeforce...Breathe in the exquisite fragrance of the velvety rose.

And now identify yourself with the rose bush and imagine that you are the rose...Know that the same life force that activates the flowering of the rose is dynamically animated in you...This miracle of development, of opening, of brilliant radiance is fully, passionately alive, replicated in your own heart-felt blossoming...Breathe in the scent of light...and breathe out the essence of enchantment...Breathe in...breathe out...and visualize a million prisms of fragrant light flowing towards the altar of your heart...A gossamer strand twirling, made up of many tiny circles of fragrant light dancing on the altar of your festive heart...Breathing in...breathing out...fragrant roses floating on the altar of your loving heart.

Inhale one more fragrant breath...The breath of the present moment...The lifebreath...The breath of the blossoming heart...Know that you are in the present moment...Call your attention to an unfamiliar and yet to be explored horizon...Feel relaxed as your inner petals unfold revealing your true inner beauty, your blossoming heart...See yourself as the source for new ideas...An inspiration for all that you cherish... Now, see before you a series of granite stepping stones...Each stone leads towards your desired future...Know that what you are seeding will blossom and grow and then be transformed into fruit...Take a step and feel the texture of the stone beneath your foot...Take another step and notice the sound your foot makes as you step on to the stone...Picture yourself taking the next step along the stepping stones of your life...And the next and the next...Know that these steps will positively enhance the choice you have made at this time...As you step upon the last stone and into your bright new future, notice who or what is around you...Now take another breath and bring yourself fully into present time...Breathe in the fragrance of the blossoming rose...Stretch out your body and be here now...and take the time to reflect on the following questions...

Pause for a Blossoming Heart

- *Having taken that step into your future who or what was around you?*

- *What new action could you take that is different from your usual life pattern?*

- *That action may not be immediately apparent.*

- *Or perhaps you need non-action!*

- *How did it feel to be stepping into your desired future?*

- *What will be your first step in bringing this to fruition.*

Instinctively, which essential oil could you use to enhance the outcome of your Rose Visualization? Take a look at the Aromatic Emotional Barometer. (page 52) Choose a positive word from the chart that you can associate with this next step and then read the relevant Essential Oil Reflection. Begin to incorporate using that essential oil in your daily energising ritual to assimilate your next step. Vaporise the oils in a diffuser or create a massage blend. You may also want to combine this essential oil with a drop of rose oil so that the two fragrances are linked together.

Enjoy the journey, prepare to be surprised and delighted as you step into the brightness of a fragrant and blossoming future.

Thank you for journeying with me through The Blossoming Heart.
May your heart always blossom and grow.

-Robbi Zeck ND

I look forward to journeying with you further in the future. For information about Aromatic Kinesiology Seminars and Aroma Tours Retreats and Tours please contact our office at:-

10 Keam Street

East Ivanhoe 3079

Victoria

Australia

Phone / Fax 61 (0)3 9499 8681

Email: robbi@aroma-tours.com

www.aromatic-kinesiology.com

www.aroma-tours.com

The Aromatic Emotional Barometer
Essential Oils at a Glance

1	ANGELICA	Assertive / Unacceptable
2	ANISEED MYRTLE	Perceptive / Incapable
3	BASIL	Expressive / Insecure
4	BENZOIN	Yielding / Resistant
5	BERGAMOT	Encouraged / Saddened
6	CEDARWOOD	Courageous / Cautious
7	GERMAN CHAMOMILE	Freedom / Imposed upon
8	CINNAMON	Connected / Withdrawn
9	CISTUS	Restored / Shocked
10	CLARY SAGE	Clarity / Stagnant
11	CLOVE BUD	Open / Controlling
12	CYPRESS	Supported / Challenged
13	ELEMI	Tranquil / Restless
14	EUCALYPTUS	Integrated / Overwhelmed
15	EVERLASTING	Adaptable / Immobilised
16	FENNEL	Completed / Unfulfilled
17	FRANKINCENSE	Protected / Vulnerable
18	GERANIUM	Attuned / Disconnected
19	GINGER	Sustained / Depleted
20	GRAPEFRUIT	Optimistic / Drained
21	JASMINE	Trusting / Fearful
22	JUNIPER	Joyful / Distressed
23	KUNZEA	Safe / Hurt
24	LAVENDER	Nurtured / Neglected
25	LEMON	Rational / Confused
26	LEMONGRASS	Expanded / Restricted

27	LIME	Calm / Agitated
28	MARJORAM	Soothed / Anxious
29	MELISSA	Grateful / Resentful
30	MYRTLE	Illuminated / Disheartened
31	NEROLI	Choice / No choice
32	NUTMEG	Revitalised / Conquered
33	ORANGE	Lighthearted / Serious
34	PALMAROSA	Compassion / Betrayed
35	PATCHOULI	Peaceful / Fragmented
36	PEPPERMINT	Purposeful / Unfocused
37	PETITGRAIN	Awakened / Stifled
38	PINE	Worthy / Inadequate
39	RAVENSARA	Definite / Tentative
40	ROSE	Loved / Isolated
41	ROSEMARY	Creative / Stuck
42	ROSEWOOD	Receptive / Hindered
43	SAGE	Wise / Unknowing
44	SANDALWOOD	Reflective / Entrenched
45	SPEARMINT	Invigorated / Weary
46	SPRUCE	Motivated / Defeated
47	TEA TREE	Understanding / Intolerant
48	SWEET THYME	Dynamic / Powerless
49	VETIVER	Assurance / Threatened
50	WINTERGREEN	Productive / Inert
51	YARROW	Balanced / Erratic
52	YLANG YLANG	Mindful / Angry

Meridian Essential Oils at a Glance

Meridian	Essential Oils
Conception Vessel	Basil, eucalyptus, grapefruit, lemongrass, rosemary, peppermint
Governing Vessel	German chamomile, frankincense, geranium, lemon, rosewood, spearmint
Stomach	Aniseed myrtle, fennel, ginger, lavender, marjoram, peppermint
Spleen	Benzoin, geranium, sweet orange, rosemary, sandalwood, vetiver
Heart	Cistus, jasmine, melissa, neroli, palmarosa, rose
Small Intestine	Cinnamon, clove bud, elemi, ginger, lavender, rosewood
Bladder	Bergamot, cedarwood, cypress, geranium, juniper, thyme
Kidney	Cedarwood, clary sage, geranium, ginger, sandalwood, spruce
Pericardium	Clary sage, jasmine, rose, sage, yarrow, ylang ylang
Triple Warmer	Angelica, geranium, lemongrass, nutmeg, patchouli, sandalwood
Gall Bladder	Basil, grapefruit, lemon, orange, rosemary, peppermint
Liver	Basil, german chamomile, everlasting, lime, rosemary, wintergreen
Lung	Eucalyptus, kunzea, myrtle, pine, ravensara, thyme
Large Intestine	Clove bud, fennel, marjoram, neroli, palmarosa, tea tree

How to Use Essential Oils

Traditionally essential oils are used in the following ways.

 MASSAGE - Add 1 drop of essential oil for each 2ml of massage oil being used. A full body massage will use about 20ml of massage oil, so mix 10 drops of essential oil into the carrier oil. This amount is approximately half a teaspoon of essential oil. Blend essential oils at half strength for children, the elderly over the age of sixty-five and pregnant women.

 BATH - Fill a bath with warm water. Add 5-8 drops of essential oil to 5mls of an emulsifier, such as full cream milk, cream or a carrier oil. Mix well. Add this blend to the water just before stepping into the bath. Use an essential oil vapouriser to add to the aromatic ambience.

 VAPORIZER - Place the vaporizer on a heatproof stand. Fill the dish with warm water, add 6-8 drops of essential oil. Light a tea-light candle and place it underneath the dish to warm and vaporise the oil. The water will evaporate as the water gently heats. There are also electric vapourizers available that do not use candles.

 INHALATION - Place a bowl on a sturdy surface. Fill the bowl with hot to boiling water. Begin by adding 2 drops and no more than 6 drops of essential oil to the water. Place a towel over the head and bowl to enclose the vapors. Inhale the vapor deeply for between 1 to 5 minutes.

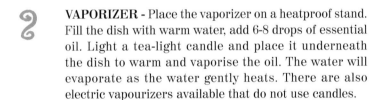 **COMPRESS** Add 2 to 6 drops of essential oil to a bowl of warm water. Mix well by agitating the water. Soak a soft cloth in the water, lightly wring it out and cover the affected area with the cloth. When doing facial compresses, take care to avoid the eyes.

 TOPICAL It is not advisable to use essential oils neat on the body with the exception of Tea Tree, which can be applied directly on bites, and Lavender, on cuts and minor burns. Otherwise mix 6-8 drops of an essential oil into 2 teaspoons of an unscented base cream and apply to affected area.

Safe Use of Essential Oils

- Keep essential oils out of reach of children.

- Do not use essential oils with babies under 6 weeks old.

- If you are pregnant or lactating always seek the
professional advice of a qualified aromatherapist.

- Do not take essential oils internally.

- Do not apply undiluted essential oils to the skin.

- Keep essential oils away from the eyes.

- Discontinue the use of essential oils if you have
an allergic reaction and seek professional advice.

- If you have medical conditions such as epilepsy,
high blood pressure, heart conditions, liver or kidney disease
or are taking medications, seek the professional
advice of a qualified aromatherapist.

- Where possible always purchase essential oils
that are 100% pure and organic.

- Essential oils should be bottled in dark glass
and stored in a safe place.

GLOSSARY OF SYMBOLS

 PLANT - Plant type and part of the plant used to produce the essential oil

 ODOUR - Odour description of the essential oil

 BLEND - Blending factor

The 'blending factor' represents the odour intensity of different essential oils. Using a scale of 1 to 10, one is the most intense odour and ten the least. For example, Bergamot has a blending factor of 10 and Basil has a blending factor of 1. When 10 drops of Bergamot are mixed with 1 drop of Basil, you have an odour that is balanced between the two essential oils.

In perfumery, this concept is more easily utilised when one is working with single aromatic compounds. Due to the complex structure of essential oils the 'blending factor' is only a guide, not an absolute formula.

The 'blending factor' does not mean that every essential oil blend must have the appropriate amount of essential oils as determined by the odour intensity. Tiny amounts of an intense essential oil, such as fennel or ylang ylang might be added to give just a hint of sweetness to a blend. At other times it can be fine to have one essential oil dominate a blend.

The 'blending factors' are a simple guide to help construct a harmonious blend of essential oils taking into account their differing odour intensities.

NOTES

While names have been changed where appropriate, the stories have been remembered to the best of my ability.

BIBLIOGRAPHY

Ackerman, Diane. *A Natural History of the Senses* Random House New York 1990

Aftel, Mandy. *Essence & Alchemy A Book of Perfume* Bloomsbury Publishing UK 2002

Allende, Isabel. *Aphrodite: A Memoir of the Senses* Harper Collins 1998

Austin, Dr. Mary. *Acupuncture Therapy* Turnstone Books UK 1974

Barille, Elisabeth. & Laroze, Catherine. *The Book of Perfume* Flammarion Paris 1995

Barnard, Julian & Martine. *The Healing Herbs of Edward Bach* Ashgrove Press UK 1998

Battaglia, S. *The Complete Guide to Aromatherapy* The Perfect Potion Qld Australia 1997

Blavatsky, H.P. *The Secret Doctrine* The Theosophical Publishing House Madras 1971

Burr, Chandler. *The Emperor of Scent* The Random House Group Ltd. UK 2003

Cabot, Dr. Sandra. *The Liver Cleansing Diet* WHAS Paddington NSW Australia 1996

Cameron, Julia. *The Artists Way* Pan Books 1995

Campbell, Joseph. *The Power of Myth* Doubleday USA 1988

Catty, Susanne. *Hydrosols: The Next Aromatherapy* Healing Arts Press 2001

Chiazzari, Suzy. *Colour Scents* The C.W. Daniel Company Ltd. 1998

Damian, Kate & Peter. *Aromatherapy: Scent and Psyche* Healing Arts Press USA 1995

Davis, Patricia. *Aromatherapy: An A-Z* C.W. Daniel Company Ltd 1995

Dowrick, Stephanie. *Intimacy and Solitude* Random House 1991

Dychtwald, Dr. K. *Bodymind* Wildwood House London 1978

Dye, Jane. *Aromatherapy for Women & Children* The C.W. Daniel Company 1992

Eden, Donna. *Energy Medicine* Piatkus UK 1999

Fanning, Patrick. *Visualization for Change* New Harbinger Publications 1994

Feldenkrais, M. *Awareness Through Movement* Harper & Row NY 1972

Fischer-Rizzi, S. *Complete Aromatherapy Handbook* Sterling 1990

Gattefosse, Rene-Maurice. *Gattefosse's Aromatherapy 1937.* C.W. Daniel Co. Ltd 1993

Gerber, Dr. Richard. *Vibrational Medicine* Bear & Company USA 1988

Gibbons, Boyd. *The Intimate Sense of Smell* National Geographic September 1986

Grieve, M. *A Modern Herbal* Penguin Books Middlesex 1982

Goleman, D. *Emotional Intelligence* Bloomsbury Publishing London 1995

Guba, Ron. *Fundamentals of Aromatic Medicine* SP 1998

Gumbel, Dr. D. *Principles of Holistic Therapy with Herbal Essences* Heidelberg Karl F. Haug 1986

Hammer, Leon. MD. *Dragon Rises. Bird Flies. Psychology and Chinese Medicine* Station Hill Press NY 1990

Harper, Jennifer. *Body Wisdom* Thorsons 1997

Hass, Dr. M. Elson. *Staying Healthy with the Seasons* Celestial Arts USA 1981

Hoffman, David. *The New Holistic Herbal* Barnes and Noble Books 1995

Holmes, Peter. *The Energetics of Western Herbs Vols.1&2* Snow Lotus Press 1997

Houston, Jean. *A Passion for the Possible* Harper San Francisco 1997

Kasmirek, Jan. *Liquid Sunshine* Floramicus UK 2002

Kaptchuk, Ted J. *Chinese Medicine: The Web Has No Weaver* Century Paperbacks 1987

Kiersey, D. & Bates, M. *Please Understand Me Character & Temperament Types* Gnosology Books USA 1984

Krebs, Charles. *A Revolutionary Way of Thinking* Melbourne Hill of Content 1998

Kumara, Shimara. *The Flowers of Life* Golden Ray Publications UK 1997

Lawless, Julia. *The Encyclopaedia of Essential Oils* Element Books 1992

Lake, Max. *Scents & Sensuality* Futura Books 1989

Leadbeater, C.W. *The Chakras* The Theosophical Publishing House Wheaton 1927

Le Guerer, A. *Scent: The Mysterious Power of Smell* Chatto & Windus 1993

Loughran, Joni Keim. & Ball, Ruah. *Aromatherapy and Subtle Energy Techniques* Frog Ltd Books USA 2000

Levy, Susan L. & Lehr, Carol. *Your Body Can Talk* HOHM Press Arizona USA 1996

Linbergh, Anne Morrow. *A Gift from the Sea* Pantheon Books New York 1995

Mailhebiau, Phillipe. *Portraits in Oils* C.W. Daniel Company Ltd 1995

Mann, Dr. Felix. *Textbook of Acupuncture* Butterworth-Heinemann 1993

McIntyre, Anne. *The Complete Floral Healer* Gaia Books London 1996

Miller, Light. N.D. & Bryan Miller. D.C. *Ayurveda and Aromatherapy* Lotus Press 1995

Mitchell, Stephen. Editor. *The Enlightened Heart* Harper Perennial 1993

Markova, Dawna. *I Will Not Die An Unlived Life* Conari Press 2000

Myss, Caroline. *Anatomy of the Spirit* Crown Publishers USA 1996

Myss, Caroline. *Why People Don't Heal and How They Can* Harmony Books New York 1999

Newman, Cathy. *Perfume the Essence of Illusion* National Geographic October 1998

Ostrander, S, & Schroeder, L. *Cosmic Memory* Simon and Schuster UK 1993

Palmer, Parker. *Let your Life Speak* Jossey-Bass Publishers USA 2000

Penoel, D & R. *Natural Home Health Care Using Essential Oils* Osmobiose 1998

Pert, Candace. *Molecules of Emotion* Scribner New York 1997

Price, Shirley. & Len. *Aromatherapy for Health Professionals* Churchill Livingstone 1995

Ray, Joni. *Sacred Flowers* Thorsons 1997

Rose, Jeanne. *The Aromatherapy Book* North Atlantic Books USA 1992

Saunders, Christine. *Essential Oil Pharmacy* Asia-Pacific Aromatherapy Hong Kong 2002

Schnaubelt. Dr. Kurt. *Medical Aromatherapy* Frog Ltd Books USA 1999

Schulz, Mona Lisa. M.D. *Awakening Intuition* Bantam Books 1998

Sheppard-Hanger S. *The Aromatherapy Practitioners Manual Vol. 1 & 2* Aquarius 1995

Stoddart, D.M. *The Scented Ape* Cambridge University Press 1990

Stokes, G. / Whiteside, D. *Touch for Health-Midday/Midnight Law* TH Enterprises CA 1981

Temelie, Barbara. *The Five Elements Wellness Plan* Sterling Publishing Company NY 2002

Thie, John. *Touch For Health- Revised edition* TH Enterprises Pasadena CA USA 1987

Tisserand, R. and Balacs, T. *Essential Oil Safety* New York: Churchill Livingstone 1995

Trungpa, Chogyam. *Shambala* Shambala Dragon Editions 1998

Muller, Julia et al. *The H & R Book of Perfume* Verlagsgesellschaft, R. Gloss & Co. Hamburg 1992

Walsh, Roger. *Essential Spirituality* John Wiley & Sons 1999

Webb, Mark. *Bush Sense* Griffin Press 2000

White, Ian. *Bush Flower Essences* Bantam Books 1991

Zeck, R. *Aromatic Kinesiology Seminars Manual Level One & Level Two* Melbourne Australia 1994

Zeck, R. *Aromatic Kinesiology Aromatherapy Today Vol. 3* Sydney Australia 1997

Zeck, R. *Aromatic Kinesiology for Healing and Transformation Aromatherapy Today Vol. 24* Australia 2002

INDEX

AROMA ✳ TOURS

Established in 1994 by Jim Llewellyn and Robbi Zeck, Aroma Tours specializes in creating unique off-the-beaten-path aromatic adventures for small groups to idyllic regions around the world.

Jim is a gastronome, sommelier, photographer and travel writer whose work is published worldwide.

Robbi is a naturopath, international trainer, author and lifestyle consultant with a busy schedule of workshops and seminars in many countries.

We have established an excellent reputation for the unique content and quality of our tours and for our friendly atmosphere and focus on personalized customer service.

One of the most common responses we receive from people is how their tour with us exceeded their expectations and as a result we enjoy a very high rate of return travellers - something we are very proud of.

Travels to awaken the senses

AROMA ✶ TOURS

Provence

Bali

Turkey

Italy

See our website for details:

www.aroma-tours.com

Aromatic Kinesiology®

The philosophy of The Blossoming Heart comes to life in the Aromatic Kinesiology seminars. Based on over twenty years of clincal research and taught in many countries around the world, Aromatic Kinesiology takes you into the world of energy and fragrance, where your heart will be opened through recognition of beauty in all its forms. Learn to apply the Essential Oil Reflections and the Aromatic Emotional Barometer as powerful tools for change.

Enhance your life skills by combining aromatherapy with kinesiology, TCM and other holistic therapies. This seminar series is an opportunity to learn effective techniques utilising the healing potency of essential oils. Learn practical techniques that will bring more energy, vitality and emotional renewal into your daily life. Aromatic Kinesiology sets a healing intention for your journey through life, using the balancing effects of essential oils as aromatic anchors for relieving emotional stress.

Reframe emotional issues with guided visualisations, affirmations and various stress management and kinesiology techniques. Create balance and harmony in your life releasing patterns that no longer serve you, so that you can shift gear from thinking negatively to expecting the best.

SOME OF THE TOPICS COVERED

- Aromatherapy as transformational medicine.

- Aromatherapy and the emotions.

- Essential oils as agents for change.

- Beauty, harmony, balance and vitality in your inner environment.

- The Essential Oil Emotional Reflections.

- The Aromatic Emotional Barometer chart.

- Essential oil emotions and the body/mind/spirit connection.

- Setting new and higher intentions for your life.

- Using visualization to create change.

- Rose visualization for future pacing.

- Improving the function of the lymphatic system.

- The physiological & psychological effects of stress.

- How stress is held in the body.

- Emotional stress release techniques.

- Re-framing emotional issues.

- Aromatic anchoring for positive change.

To find out more please visit our website:

www.aromatic-kinesiology.com

The
Blossoming
Heart

Robbi Zeck ND

Aromatherapy
for Healing and
Transformation

If you would like to order copies of **The Blossoming Heart**
please contact the Aroma Tours office at:

10 Keam Street East Ivanhoe 3079 Victoria Australia

Phone/Fax +61 (03) 9499 8681 Email: robbi@aroma-tours.com

www.aromatic-kinesiology.com
www.aroma-tours.com

Notes

Notes

Notes

Notes